S0-ARC-768

Celestial Navigation
for Yachtsmen

Mary Blewitt

ADLARD COLES NAUTICAL
London

ACKNOWLEDGEMENTS

The tables in Appendices A-E from *The Nautical Almanac*, and those in Appendices E-H from AP3270 (HO249) *Sight Reduction Tables for Air Navigation* are copyright of the Particle Physics and Astronomy Research Council and are reproduced by permission of The Council for the Central Laboratory for the Research Councils.

Published by Adlard Coles Nautical
an imprint of A & C Black Publishers Ltd
38 Soho Square, London W1D 3HB
www.adlardcoles.com

Copyright © Mary Blewitt 1997

First published 1950 for Yachting World
Editions in 1957, 1968, 1971, 1975, 1978, 1980, 1986, 1987

Tenth edition published by Nautical Books 1990
Reprinted by Adlard Coles Nautical 1993
Eleventh edition published by Adlard Coles Nautical 1997
Reissued 2004

ISBN 978-0-7136-8938-9

All rights reserved. No part of this publication may be reproduced in any form or by any means – graphic, electronic or mechanical, including photocopying, recording, taping or information storage and retrieval systems – without the prior permission in writing of the publishers.

A CIP catalogue for this book is available from the British Library.

A & C Black uses paper produced with elemental chlorine-free pulp, harvested from managed sustainable forests

Printed and bound in Great Britain by Caligraving

Note: While all reasonable care has been taken in the publication of this book, the publisher takes no responsibility for the use of the methods or products described in the book.

Forewords

I am glad to be able to contribute a short foreword to this book because, having studied the text, I am sure that it will satisfy the very real need for an up-to-date work based on the use of the simplified tables and written entirely from the yachtsman's, as opposed to the airman's or ship navigator's, point of view.

Rigorous exclusion of unnecessary material from the text has, in my view, added to the value of the book and made it easier to attain that most desirable thing—correct emphasis on the various aspects of the subject. The result is lucid and practical, but there is just sufficient theoretical explanation included to inculcate the knowledge that is necessary as a basis for this subject.

By the late Captain (E) J. H. Illingworth, R.N.

When Mary Blewitt wrote her admirably concise guide to the principles and practice of astro-navigation at sea, shortly after the war, methods of sight reduction had already become greatly simplified by the introduction of direct-entry (Alt./Az) tables and the GHA almanac. She was at that time a successful navigator in ocean races, in such famous craft as *Bloodhound* and *Myth of Malham*; and her severely practical aim was to provide the yachtsman with sufficient information to make the best possible use of his sextant, timepiece and tables. The book has stood the test of time and, through successive revisions and changes in navigational practice, continues to give sound advice on the whole matter of sights at sea. It has now in effect become a standard work.

The author, as Mary Pera, was later to become Secretary of the Royal Ocean Racing Club and, in due course, Chairman of the Racing Rules Committee of the Royal Yachting Association. Her contributions to navigation have been many, but none has perhaps been more abiding than this seaman-like little volume.

By M. W. Richey, former Director of The Royal Institute of Navigation

Preface

Since the first edition of this book in 1950 very large changes have taken place in the yachting scene, and even larger ones in the field of navigation. In the past, to circumnavigate the world without 'astro' would have been a dangerous hit-or-miss performance. Today, yachts race round the world and across oceans with batteries of computers supplying positions from GPS and other navigational aids without any apparent need for astro. This is fine, provided of course, and it is a very important proviso, that the instruments function correctly and that the batteries stay in a condition to operate the electronic equipment. To say that ocean voyaging is safer with the new instruments is a truism, but just as a driver needs contingency plans for when he has a flat tyre, so a navigator needs a fall-back when his instruments let him down. Offshore, that fall-back must be astro. When the crisis occurs, this book will help lighten the darkness of the navigator struggling with almanac and tables, perhaps for the very first time.

There used to be a tendency among navigators to parade celestial navigation as a black art, too difficult for the ordinary chap to understand, but those days are long gone and with the arrival of computers the new generations are less frightened of figures than their forebears. I have written for beginners – or for those who have forgotten all they knew – and I have presumed them to be as ignorant and confused as I was when I began. However, since, in fact, the reader need only add and subtract, he will not find the subject too complicated. As with all navigation, the most difficult part is judging the accuracy of the information obtained, and assessing the weight that can be put on it. If the navigator does not know whether his position line (however obtained) is one mile out or twenty, it is as if he had never taken a sight. The reader's real work will begin after he has absorbed this book and begins to observe often enough to form his own opinion of the value of his sights. It must be fun, in these days of GPS, to have a competition on board as to who can take the most accurate sight, and of course work it out. Now that checking the accuracy of sights is easy there should be more incentive to practice.

To avoid unnecessary detail, some of the statements are slightly inaccurate. For instance, I say that one nautical mile equals one minute of arc on the Earth's surface: this is not strictly true, for the measurement varies at the poles and the equator, but the difference is never apparent in practical navigation. For simplicity, I have left out any mention of such technicalities as the celestial equator or the celestial horizon. The reader who wishes to study the subject more thoroughly must turn to the *Admiralty Manual of Navigation* or similar publications

The *Nautical Almanac* and the Air Tables (AP3270) are used for the examples because they are the simplest and least specialised. Mixing marine and air systems brings some inevitable inconsistencies, but nothing that need trouble the yachtsman. As an added bonus, the *Nautical Almanac* now carries concise tables which allow it to be used alone, although I should not advise this to begin with. Another almanac, published by Adlard Coles Nautical, also contains in one volume all the necessary ephemeral data together with its own sight reduction system; this is *Reeds Astro Navigation Tables* compiled by Cdr Harry Baker.

Few amateurs can hope to reach the standard of a professional navigator – or should I say old-time professional navigator? Regular daily observations over the years ensured confidence and accuracy; but this does not mean that you will not be able to take adequately competent sights, even in rough seas, and I can assure you that a sense of triumph when a sight proves correct is well worth the effort involved. It is the first step that is difficult; take one sight and you will be bewildered, take two and the fog begins to clear, take a dozen and you will wonder what all the fuss was about. I hope that the explanations in this book are clear enough to encourage you to go and take a sight with a good idea of what you are trying to do and modicum of confidence that you will be able to do it.

Mary Blewitt
1997

Contents

KEY TO THE DIAGRAMS

The key applies to all the diagrams in this book.
P, P'   North and South Poles
E, E'   Equator
H, H'   Horizon
Q   Centre of the Earth
X   Geographical position of the heavenly body under discussion
Z   The observer, or the azimuth angle at the observer
Z'   Observer's zenith
G   Any point on the Greenwich meridian

From the foregoing it follows that—
The line PZ is part of the observer's meridian.
The line PX is part of the meridian of the geographical position of the heavenly body under discussion.
The line PG is part of the Greenwich meridian.
Except where further description is necessary these letters are not explained again in the book.

ABBREVIATIONS

BST   British Summer Time
DR   Dead reckoning
GHA   Greenwich hour angle
GMT   Greenwich Mean Time
UT   Universal Time
GP   Geographical position
IE   Index error
LHA   Local hour angle
SD   Semi-diameter
AP   Air Publication (Air Ministry)
NP   Nautical Publication
HD   Hydrographic Department (Admiralty)
HO   Hydrographic Office (US Naval Oceanographic Office)
Zn   Azimuth
Hs   (Height sextant) Sextant altitude
Ho   (Height observed) Corrected sextant altitude, or True altitude
Hc   (Height calculated) Tabulated attitude

The Theory

The Heavenly Bodies

Before the theory of a sight can be understood, there are facts about the Earth you must grasp and terms you must learn.

We navigate by means of the Sun, the Moon, the planets and the stars. Forget how the Earth spins round the Sun with the motionless stars inconceivable distances away; imagine instead that the Earth is the centre of the universe and that all the heavenly bodies circle slowly round us, the stars keeping their relative positions while the Sun, Moon and planets change their positions in relation to each other and to the stars. This pre-Copernican outlook comes easily as we watch the heavenly bodies rise and set, and is a help in practical navigation.

The Geographical Position (GP)

At any moment of the day or night there is some spot on the Earth's surface that is directly underneath the Sun. This is the Sun's GP, and it lies where a line drawn from the centre of the Earth to the Sun cuts the Earth's surface. It is shown in Fig 1 at X. Not only the Sun but all heavenly bodies have GPs, and these positions can be found from the Almanac at any given moment. The GP is measured by declination and hour angle.

Declination

The declination of a heavenly body is the latitude of its GP, and is measured exactly as latitude, in degrees north or south of the equator. The Sun's declination moves from 23°N in midsummer when it reaches the tropic of Cancer, to 23°S in midwinter at the tropic of Capricorn; in the spring and autumn, at the equinoxes, the declination is 0° as the Sun crosses the equator. The declination of the Sun alters, on average, one degree every four days throughout the year, but the rate of change varies. During the summer solstice in 1997 for example, it takes 34 days for the Sun to climb 1° up and then lose that degree from its peak on midsummer's day: it is indeed well named the solstice (sol = sun, stit = stat as in station). On the other hand, at the equinox, when days and nights are of equal length, the declination changes by two degrees in only five days. Fig 2 shows how declination and latitude are measured as angles at

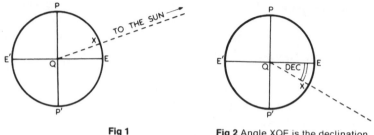

Fig 1   **Fig 2** Angle XQE is the declination
of X; it is about 23° S.

the centre of the Earth. Q is the centre of the Earth; E a point on the equator immediately north of X; and X, as we have seen, is the GP of the Sun. Since by eye we can see that the Sun is far south, the time of year must be about midwinter.

The Moon's declination varies between 28°30′N and S; it changes rapidly, sometimes as much as six or seven degrees in 24 hours. The declinations of the planets change slowly and always lie in a band between 29°N and S. The declinations of the stars are virtually fixed, varying by less than one minute of arc (1′) during the year.

The declinations of those heavenly bodies suitable for navigation are found in the Almanac for every hour of the day and can be interpolated to an accuracy of a tenth of a minute (0′.1).

Hour Angle

The GP of any heavenly body is not only on a parallel of latitude but also on a meridian of longitude, and hour angle is the method of measuring this meridian. It differs from longitude in some marked respects.

Let us consider the Sun. You are at the Old Royal Observatory (or any-where else north of N23°), standing on the Greenwich meridian: when the Sun is due south of you (about noon), its hour angle is nil. Two hours later its hour angle is two hours; and as the Sun sets, goes round to the other side of the Earth and rises again, the hour angle increases until at eleven in the morning it is 23 hours while at noon it comes the full circle of 24 hours to start again at zero as it crosses the meridian. The hour angle, when it is measured from the Greenwich meridian is called Greenwich Hour Angle (GHA). GHA is always measured in a westerly direction from the meridian of Green-wich to the meridian of the GP of the heavenly body concerned. It can be measured in time or in arc (degrees, minutes and seconds): once round the Earth is 24 hours or 360°.

You might well think that you could tell how far round the Sun had gone since midday and measure hour angle just by looking at an accurate quartz watch, but this is not so. The Sun does not keep regular, or mean, time; it can occasionally be as much as 20 minutes fast or slow on Greenwich Mean Time, so that the GHA of the Sun has to be looked up in the Almanac where it can be found for every hour, minute and second of every day. GMT is now known throughout the world as UT, Universal Time, and will be referred to as such in this book. (It is interesting that since time signals are no longer based on celestial motions but on an atomic time-scale there is a maximum correction of 0.9 of a second to be applied to longitude for those aiming at maximum accuracy—it need not bother us!)

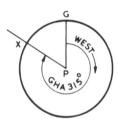

Fig 3

In Fig 3 we are looking down on to the North Pole. The GHA of the Sun is measured west from the Greenwich meridian, as shown by the arrow. It is morning, for the Sun is coming up to Greenwich and the GHA is approximately 21 hours or 315° (360° = 24h, so 15° = 1h).

Hour angle can be measured not only from the Greenwich meridian but from any meridian. When it is measured from the meridian on which you, the observer, are standing, it is known as Local Hour Angle (LHA); this, too, is measured in a westerly direction. When you are west of Greenwich, LHA is less than GHA because the Sun passed Greenwich before it passed you, and so GHA is the larger angle. When you are east of Greenwich, LHA is greater than GHA since the Sun passed you first. Whereas GHA is found from the Almanac, LHA is found by adding or subtracting your longitude to, or from, GHA.

(At this point you may well ask: how can I add or subtract my longitude when it is precisely what I am trying to determine? It is a fair question, but just for the moment accept—pretend—that you do know it, and later on you will see why you can make that assumption.)

Consider the examples in Figs 4–7. The workings apply not only in the northern hemisphere but also in the southern, indeed from any point on the meridians in question.

Example A (Fig 4)

You are somewhere in Canada (Long. 75°W) at 1300 local time. As it is one hour after your noon the Sun will be an hour past your meridian and the LHA (heavy line) will be 1 hour. But it is a long time since the Sun crossed the Greenwich meridian, so the GHA (unbroken line) will be much larger. It will be the 75° of your longitude (broken line) plus the 15° the Sun has gone past you, ie 90° (6 hours). In west longitudes:

$$GHA - observer's\ longitude = LHA$$
$$90° - 75° = 15°$$

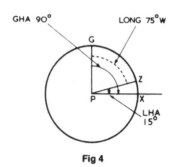

Fig 4

Example B (Fig 5)

You are in Italy (Long. 15°E) at 1100 local time. Since it is an hour before your noon, LHA (heavy line) is 23 hours or 345°. The Sun has further to go, however, to reach the Greenwich meridian, so GHA (unbroken line) is only 22 hours or 330°. In east longitudes:

$$GHA + observer's\ longitude = LHA$$
$$330° + 15° = 345°$$

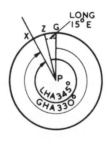

Fig 5

12

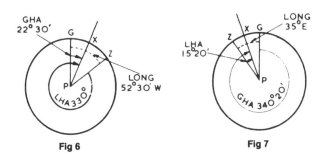

Fig 6   Fig 7

Example C (Fig 6)

You are somewhere in the Atlantic and the Sun has just passed the Greenwich meridian so that GHA is only 1h 30m or 22°30′; but the Sun has not yet reached your meridian PZ (52°30′W). On that meridian it is only 1000 and LHA will be 22 hours or 330°. In spite of this the rule holds good; the observer is west of Greenwich so:

$$\text{GHA} - \text{observer's longitude} = \text{LHA}$$

but because the subtraction is impossible as it stands (22°30′–52°30′) we must add 360° to the GHA to get:

$$382°30′–52°30′ = 330°$$

Example D (Fig 7)

You are in the eastern Mediterranean (Long 35°E). The Sun has passed your meridian but has not yet reached Greenwich. LHA therefore is small but GHA is large, 340°20′ or 22h 41m 20″. Now your longitude is east of Greenwich so:

$$\text{GHA} + \text{observer's longitude} = \text{LHA}$$
$$340°20′ + 35° = 375°20′$$

When, as here, the resulting figure is more than 360°, 360 must be subtracted from the total, giving LHA 15°20′. We can now say that:

$$\text{LHA} = \text{GHA} \; {+\,\text{east} \atop -\,\text{west}} \; \text{longitude}$$

When, with an easterly longitude, the total comes to more than 360°, that sum (or even occasionally as we shall see a multiple of that sum) is subtracted to arrive at LHA. With a westerly longitude, when GHA is less than the observer's longitude, 360° are added to GHA to make the subtraction possible.

13

These diagrams hold good not only for the Sun but for all heavenly bodies although only the Sun crosses the Greenwich meridian at approximately 12h UT. The daily times of the meridian passages at Greenwich of the Moon and useful planets are given in the Almanac. More importantly, the Almanac tabulates the GHA of those planets, for the Moon and for the 'First Point of Aries' from which the GHAs of the stars can be calculated (see p 41).

Hour angle differs from longitude in three main ways:

1. HA can always be measured in time or in arc, and conversion tables are to be found in all almanacs and most tables.
2. HA is *always* measured in a westerly direction.
3. HA may be:
    (a) GHA, measured from the Greenwich meridian;
    (b) LHA, measured from the meridian of the observer; or
    (c) Sidereal Hour Angle (SHA). This is explained later on p 41.

For any given second, the GHA of any heavenly body useful to navigation can be found in the Almanac and its LHA can be derived by adding or subtracting the longitude of the observer to, or from, GHA.

To return for a moment to the GP, it should now be clear that the GP of any heavenly body is determined by declination and GHA, and that this GP could be plotted on a map, although in fact it is never necessary to do so. As an exercise, try to guess where the GP of the Sun is at the moment you read this. I, for instance, am writing almost on the Greenwich meridian on 17 August at 1635 UT so the Sun passed me 4h 35m ago, its GP lies about longitude 68°W. Its declination and therefore the latitude of its GP, I guess to be N15° (actually N 13°21', W 67°44'). The sun was over the Caribbean Sea when I started my mental arithmetic, but it travels at a great pace and the plot of its GP is instantly out of date.

The Zenith

If a line were drawn from the centre of the Earth through you and out into space, it would lead to your zenith. In other words, it is the point in space immediately above your head. For instance if you were standing at the GP of the Sun, then the Sun would be in your zenith.

The Horizon

As it is impossible to see round a corner we cannot see much of the surface of the Earth which bends away from us in all directions. The horizon lies in a

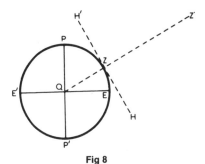

Fig 8

plane which at sea level is at a tangent to the Earth's surface. This plane is at right angles to the direction of the observer's zenith. In Fig 8 HH′ is a tangent to the Earth's surface at Z and both ∠ Z′ZH and ∠ Z′ZH′ are right angles.

Altitude

The altitude is the angle made at the observer between the Sun (or any other heavenly body) and the horizon directly below it. In Fig 9 ∠ HZS is the altitude of the Sun. This is the angle you measure when you take a sight.

Zenith Distance

The zenith distance is the complement of the altitude. In Fig 9 it is ∠ Z′ZS.

Altitude + zenith distance = 90°

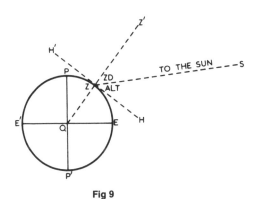

Fig 9

15

The Elevated Pole

The pole nearer to the observer is called the elevated pole : the North Pole in the northern and the South Pole in the southern hemisphere.

Azimuth and Azimuth Angle

The azimuth is the bearing (true *not* magnetic) of a heavenly body. This bearing may be called azimuth (Zn) or azimuth angle (Z) depending on the method of measurement. Azimuth angles are measured eastwards or westwards from north or south according to the elevated pole: in the northern hemisphere from N to 179°E and from N to 179°W. Fig 10 shows a number of azimuth angles in the northern hemisphere.

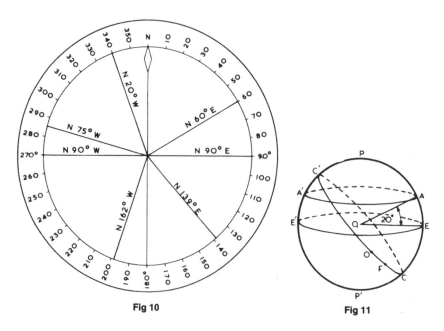

Fig 10   Fig 11

When working out a sight, azimuth is obtained from the tables where a single figure is found; this may be N145°E or N145°W depending on whether the heavenly body has passed your meridian or not. For example, in the morning the azimuth angle of the Sun will be N and E, in the afternoon, N and W. To convert the azimuth angle into azimuth (the bearing measured from north through east from 0° to 360°), the rule in northern latitudes is:

LHA greater than 180° .... Z = Zn

LHA less than 180° .... 360° − Z = Zn

This rule is given on each page of the tables together with the rule for the southern hemisphere. To take an example, in Lat N50° with the LHA 22° (afternoon, with the Sun to the west) and Z145°, then:

$$360° - 145° = 215° = Zn$$

Had you looked along your compass when you took your sight and allowed for magnetic variation, you would have found the Sun on a bearing of 215°. It is never possible, however, to measure azimuth accurately enough with a compass and it must be extracted from the tables.

Great Circles

A great circle is any circle with its centre the centre of the Earth and its radius the distance from the centre to the surface of the Earth. The equator and the meridians are great circles, but the parallels of latitude, except the equator, are not, because the centre of a circle formed by a parallel of latitude lies either north or south of the centre of the Earth. Distances along a great circle can be measured in two ways, in miles or by the angle subtended at the centre of the Earth.

The shortest distance between any two points on the Earth's surface lies along a great circle, and with a globe and a piece of string, you can see roughly where the great circle runs between, say, Glasgow and New York, or Los Angeles and Sydney, by holding one end of the string on one place and pulling it as tight as possible to the other.

In Fig 11 three great circles are shown: EE', CC' and the circle PEP'E' on which A and E lie; AA' is a parallel of latitude but not a great circle. Since we have said that A and E are on the same meridian, the distance AE can be expressed in two ways: in arc it makes an angle of 20° at Q (the latitude of A is also 20°); in miles, since one minute of arc (1') subtended at Q makes one nautical mile (1nm) at the Earth's surface, AE = 20x60 = 1200nm.

CC' is a great circle (although it is not a meridian, for it does not pass through the poles), and therefore the distance, if known, between O and F, two points on that circle, could also be expressed in miles or arc. These methods of measurement, or of expressing the measurement, can be used between any two points on the Earth's surface and the interchangeability of arc and mileage should always be kept in mind.

Universal Time (UT)

UT (formerly GMT) is an average, or mean, of the Sun's time, necessary because the Sun rarely crosses the Greenwich meridian at 12h UT, routinely arriving early or late throughout the year. The almanac gives the 'Equation of Time' (E) for midnight and noon daily, showing by how much the Sun differs from UT. The time of the meridian passage alongside tells us if it is fast or slow. For example, at noon on 8 December 1997 (see Appendix B), E is 08m 04s and the meridian passage (to the nearest minute) 11h 52m, telling us that the Sun is over 8 minutes slow on UT.

At this stage, I advise readers to whom all this is new to re-read what has been written so far, because it is important to understand it thoroughly before tackling the next sections.

The Position Line

The final result obtained from any sight on any heavenly body is a straight line on your chart, and you are somewhere on that line. When the Sun is in your zenith its altitude is 90°, and there is only one spot on the Earth's surface where you can be: at the GP of the Sun. As you move away from the GP (or rather as it moves rapidly away from you) the altitude will lessen, and it will lessen equally whether you go north, south, east or west. However far you move you are on a 'position circle' with its centre at the GP, on which every point is equidistant from the GP and every altitude of the Sun the same. Fig 12 shows how the rays from the Sun, or from any other heavenly body, strike the Earth. The GP is at X and we see that the further the observer is from X the larger the 'position circle' and the lower the altitude. The altitude lessens until the Sun disappears below the horizon, when its altitude is 0° and zenith distance 90°.

Fig 13 shows a 'position circle' and an azimuth from the observer to the GP; the Sun is to the SW of the observer, who will therefore be on the NE portion of the circle. Unfortunately you cannot obtain the azimuth of the Sun accurately enough to fix your exact position on the circle. The only thing to do is to draw a line at right angles to the most accurate azimuth available and say 'I am somewhere on this line'. The line is drawn straight because the distance from the centre of the circle is so great that it is impossible to show the curve of the circle on the chart.

It may be helpful to realise how very large these 'position circles' are. For example, on a winter's morning, when the Sun is over SW Africa, its altitude

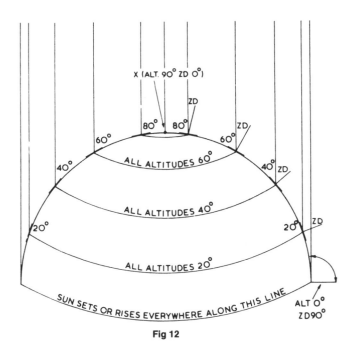

Fig 12

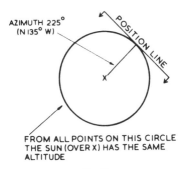

Fig 13

19

in England is about 12° and it has the same altitude in the following places: Greenwich, the Caspian Sea, Madras, the South Pole, Chile, Guiana and the Azores. Even in midsummer at noon, when the Sun is at its highest (63°) and nearest to England, the circle runs through Greenwich, Istanbul, Cairo, Congo, the Cape Verde Islands and the Azores.

The fact that the position line is at right angles to the azimuth is of practical value not only for working out sights but also for choosing the best time to take them. In Fig 14 you are approaching a strange coast from the NW and are not certain of your position. A morning sight of the Sun when it bears SE might give you the line AA', determining your distance off the land; while from a sight in the afternoon, line BB' positions you along the coast.

The Meridian Passage

When a heavenly body crosses the meridian of the observer, either to the north or to the south of him, an excellent opportunity occurs for an easy sight, for two reasons. First, no plotting is required. A position line, as we have seen, lies at right angles to the bearing of the heavenly body under observation, so when the body crosses your meridian, ie is due north or south of you, your position line will run east and west, and a line running east and west is a parallel of latitude. Secondly, accurate time is not required because the moment of passage is when the altitude of the body is at its highest. Such observations are most commonly used for the Sun—a 'noon sight'—and for *Polaris*, the Pole Star, which is more or less permanently on everyone's meridian to the north.

There are four cases, similar in principle:

Case 1, Fig 15

Every heavenly body is so far from the Earth that its rays strike the Earth in parallel lines (but see p 27), a band of light rather than a cone as was shown in Fig 12. In Fig 15, PZXP' is the meridian on which both Z and X lie. Two parallel rays from the Sun, SZ and S'XQ, hit the meridian at Z and X, and cross the straight line Z'ZQ. It follows that $\angle Z'ZS$ and $\angle ZQX$ are equal. Now $\angle Z'ZS$ is the zenith distance, so when we observe the altitude of the Sun we learn the size of this angle (90°-Alt = ZD). From the Almanac we can find $\angle XQE$ for it is the declination. Add $\angle ZQX$ and $\angle XQE$ and the resulting $\angle ZQE$ is the latitude of Z.

$$\text{Latitude} = \text{Zenith Distance} + \text{Declination}$$
$$\text{LAT} = \text{ZD} + \text{DEC}$$

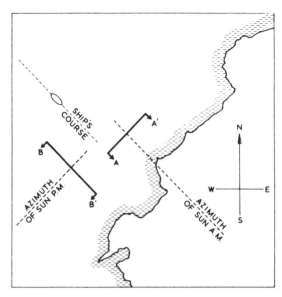

Fig 14

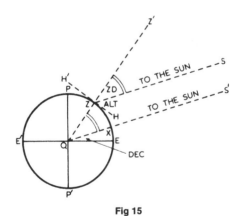

Fig 15

Case 2, Fig 16

The observer at Z is taking a noon sight of the Sun (at X and on the same meridian). X is south of the equator so the declination is south, and we can see here that $\angle$ ZQX includes $\angle$ EQX and so the latitude of Z = $\angle$ ZXQ – $\angle$ EQX; that is, Latitude = Zenith Distance – Declination.

$$LAT = ZD - DEC$$

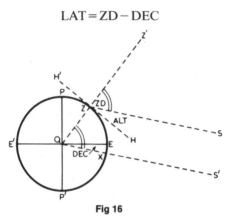

Fig 16

When declination and latitude are both north or both south the situation is known as *same* name; when one is north and the other south it is called *contrary* name. We can therefore say, in Cases 1 and 2 where the observer is between the body observed (here the Sun) and the elevated pole, that:

$$\text{Latitude} = \text{Zenith Distance} \begin{array}{c} +(\text{same name}) \\ \\ -(\text{contrary name}) \end{array} \text{Declination}$$

$$LAT = ZD \pm DEC$$

Case 3, Fig 17

The third case is where the GP of the body observed is between the observer and the elevated pole. Once again $\angle$ Z'ZS = $\angle$ ZQX. $\angle$ XQE, the declination, consists of $\angle$ ZQX + ZQE, the observer's latitude, so:

$$\text{Latitude} = \text{Declination} - \text{Zenith Distance}$$
$$LAT = DEC - ZD$$

Observations of *Polaris* present good examples of this configuration and are useful because, as with other meridian sights, accurate time is not necessary while the star is always available, only a few minor corrections being required to adjust for its not being precisely over the North Pole.

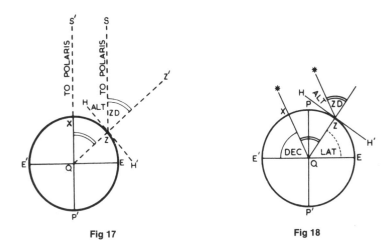

Fig 17   **Fig 18**

Case 4, Fig 18

One further case occurs, mainly in far northern or southern latitudes, when the observer and the GP of the body observed are on opposite sides of the elevated pole: then

$$L = 180° - (DEC + ZD)$$

Spherical Triangles

We have seen that in each of the last four diagrams the zenith distance is equal to the angle subtended at the Earth's centre by the observer and the GP. This is true not only of noon sights or observations of *Polaris*, when the GP is due north or south of the observer, but of all sights, whatever the bearing of the heavenly body. The zenith distance *always* equals the angle at the Earth's centre made by the GP and the observer. Looking again at Figs 15–18, ∠ ZQX will always equal ZD even when the two points Z and X no longer lie on a meridian but on some other great circle. This angle can be translated into miles at the Earth's surface: an altitude of 47° gives a zenith distance of 43° which, since 1′ of arc = 1nm, means that the GP is 43x60 = 2580 miles away from the observer.

We now know that by taking a sight and finding the zenith distance we can find our distance from the GP of any visible body (provided its particulars are tabled in the Almanac), but because the distances involved are so huge, we cannot put a compass on the GP and draw the required circle. Nor can we mark the position line on our charts except when the body is on our meridian and the distances are conveniently marked by parallels of latitude.

We must therefore approach the problem from a different direction. We pretend that we do not know the altitude of the heavenly body (although we have just measured it) but that we *do* know where we are. We assume we know our latitude and longitude and we work from an *assumed position* (sometimes called the 'chosen position').

In Fig 19 we are looking at the outside of the Earth; PAP′ and PBP′ are the meridians of X and Z crossing the equator at A and B. What do we know about the triangle PZX? We know the length of the *d* PZ; BZ is the observer's (assumed) latitude, therefore:

$$PZ = 90° - \text{Latitude of observer}$$

We know the length of the side PX; AX is the declination, therefore:

$$PX = 90° - \text{Declination of heavenly body observed.}$$

We know the size of the included angle ZPX, since this is the local hour angle (the angle between the observer's meridian and the meridian of the GP measured in a westerly direction).

Now if we know two sides and the included angle of a triangle, we can by means of spherical trigonometry, or by tables, find out the length of the side XZ and the other two angles. The length of the side XZ is equal to the zenith distance, so that $90°-XZ = \text{Altitude}$. Since this figure is found in the tables it is called the *tabulated altitude* (or calculated altitude). Had we taken a perfect sight at our assumed position at that particular time we should have got the same figure from our sextant—the true altitude (see p 27).

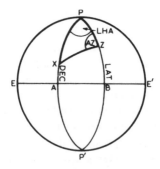

Fig 19

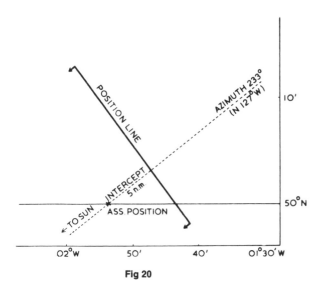

Fig 20

The Intercept

Imagine that we take a sight of the Sun with a true altitude of 41°38′ from the sextant. We know we are somewhere southwest of the Isle of Wight and we assume that our position is N50°00′ W01°54′ (the reasons why we choose this position rather than another will become apparent later). After the necessary calculations, we get a tabulated altitude from the tables of 41°43′. If we had been at the assumed position, our true altitude also would have been 41°43′, but it was not, so we are somewhere else. The difference between the tabulated altitude and the true altitude is 5′ and, since 5′ = 5nm, our position line will be 5 miles away from the assumed position. This is called an *intercept* of 5 miles.

If you look again at Fig 19 you will see that ∠ PZX is the azimuth which can now be estimated. For the sight we have just taken, the tables tell us that the azimuth angle Z was 127°, and because it was afternoon we know this was N127°W (Zn 233°). We now mark our assumed position on the chart (Fig 20) and draw the azimuth through it. As has already been explained, the position line lies at right angles to the azimuth, the intercept was 5 miles, so, from our assumed position, our position line will be 5nm *away* from or *towards* the Sun. The further we move away from the GP the less the altitude, so if our true altitude was less than our tabulated altitude we must have been further away than we assumed. In this case the tabulated altitude was 41°43′, the true altitude 41°38′, so the position line will be away from the Sun. The position

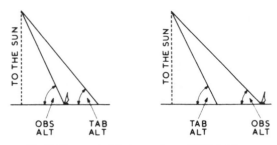

Fig 21 Observed altitude greater ... TOWARDS.
Observed altitude less ... AWAY.

line can be drawn, as shown, with little arrows pointing towards the body observed which helps to stop you making a mistake; the real reason is discussed on p 48. Fig 21 shows the principle of the intercept schematically.

Fig 22 shows another example of the triangle which must always be solved. Here X is the GP of the Sun. From merely looking at this triangle we can tell certain things: it is morning at Z, for the Sun is to the east, and it is winter for the Sun's declination is south of the equator. Now PZ = 90° − Latitude of the observer; PX = 90° + Declination, and ∠ ZPX = LHA. In this case LHA, measured west from the meridian of Z, is (say) 323° and the internal angle (ZPX) is 360° − 323° = 37°; but the tables will look after all that for us and the important point is that we know the size of the angle. ZX and ∠ PZX can now be calculated and the tabulated altitude (90° − ZX) and the azimuth angle found in the tables.

This is the principle of every sight taken—that with the known facts about a heavenly body and an assumed position we can calculate an altitude, and that as the tabulated altitude varies from the true altitude so the fulcrum of the position line varies from the assumed position.

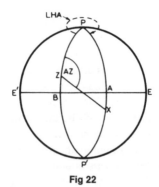

Fig 22

Sextant Altitude and True Altitude

When you take a sight, the angle you read off from your sextant is called the sextant altitude (Hs), to which certain corrections must be applied to obtain true altitude (Ho). It is true altitude that is compared with the tabulated altitude (Hc). The abbreviations stand for 'height sextant', 'height observed' and 'height calculated'.

Dip (height of eye) The tabulated altitude in the tables is given as if you were at sea level, but at sea your eye may be 6 or 60 feet above it depending on whether you are in a yacht or a liner. The correction must be made to the sextant altitude to make it a sea-level reading; in small boats it is usually about –3'. It must be applied to all sights except those taken with a bubble sextant or an artificial horizon.

Refraction Just as a pencil appears to bend when you put it in a glass of water, the rays of light from heavenly bodies are bent, or refracted, when passing through the Earth's atmosphere. The lower the altitude of the body, the greater is the refraction. Sights below 6° are inadvisable and those below 10° should be treated with caution. A correction for refraction must be applied to all sights.

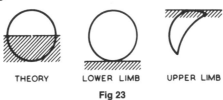

THEORY   LOWER LIMB   UPPER LIMB

Fig 23

Semi-Diameter (Fig 23) This correction applies only to the Sun and Moon. In theory, when taking a sight, the horizon should bisect the 'body', but this is impractical and when observing the Sun the bottom or *lower* limb is usually rested on the horizon; the Sun's *upper* limb can be used if the lower limb is hidden by clouds. With the Moon, the limb used depends on which is available. In each case half the diameter of the body must be allowed for. Semi-diameter is given in the Almanac every three days for both Sun and Moon. The correction, usually about 16', is added for the lower and subtracted for the upper; but not with a bubble sextant or artificial horizon.

Parallax It was said earlier that the rays from heavenly bodies strike the Earth in parallel. This is not strictly true, but as far as the Sun, stars and planets are concerned the parallax correction is negligible and can be ignored. The Moon, however, is so much nearer to the Earth that a considerable correction is often necessary; it is called *horizontal parallax* (HP) or *parallax in altitude* (P in A) and is tabulated in the Almanac.

The Practice

Almanacs and Tables

The practice of working out a sight can be broken down into two distinct parts: first, locating the position of the body observed at that particular moment on that particular day in that year when you took your sight, information that must come from an almanac; and, secondly, reducing the spherical triangle so found, for which tables or a calculator are necessary. Any almanac (including one stored in a calculator) can be used with any tables and vice versa, although certain tables and almanacs are designed to be used together. Most calculators can replace tables, some resolving the triangle more easily than others.

Almanacs

There are temporary publications, also called ephemerides, which must be renewed every year. They give the positions (GHA and declination) of the heavenly bodies throughout the year, as well as additional information such as times of sunrise and sunset, eclipses, the Moon's phases etc. You need only one almanac, but there are several to choose from.

The Nautical Almanac, used for the examples in this book, is published in one volume for the year; it is designed for marine use and gives the required information in a compact and simple way. It has one section to help those using calculators, and also a set of tables called Concise Sight Reduction Tables which, although more complex than those used for the examples in this book, allows a sailor to dispense with any other tables.

The Air Almanac, as its title implies, is designed for use in aircraft. It is easy to use and if you find it on board you will have no difficulty in adapting from the *Nautical Almanac*, but it is expensive.

Reeds Astro Navigation Tables (see page 56) contains in one volume all the information required for its own method of reduction.

A navigator who has absorbed the principles of celestial navigation will have little trouble in following any available almanac.

Tables

Astronomical tables never go out of date, with the one exception of AP3270

Vol 1 which covers only nine years. Modern tables are entered with LHA declination and latitude to find tabulated altitude and azimuth. They solve the innumerable variations of the triangle. (For pure interest, HD486 has 720 solutions to a full page, 360 pages to a volume and six volumes, making a total of probably about one and a quarter million solutions.) Three sets of tables are available for the yacht navigator.

Sight Reduction Tables for Air Navigation (AP3270, HO249) are the tables used for the examples in this book. They consist of three volumes, each 31x26cm, based on epochs.

Vol 1 Selected Stars
Vol 2 Latitudes 0°–39°, Declinations 0°–29°
Vol 3 Latitudes 40°–89°, Declinations 0°–29°

Sight Reduction Tables for Marine Navigation (NP401, HO229) are designed for use with the *Nautical Almanac*. The tables consist of six volumes, each covering 16° of latitude and declination from 0°-90°. They are about the same size as AP3270. These tables are more accurate than HD486 (HO214) which they replaced, but such accuracy is of no great advantage in elementary yacht navigation. Those used to AP3270 will be able to adapt to either NP401 or HD486 if they want to change over to one of them.

Concise Sight Reduction Tables. As we said above, these are tables printed at the back of the *Nautical Almanac*. They are discussed on page 55.

A Sun Sight in Winter

Using the Sextant

Let us pretend you are in the North Sea, DR position N51°56′, E1°51′, on the morning of 7 December 1997 and that you wish to take a sun sight.

In order to work out your sight, you need two things: the sextant altitude of the Sun and the exact time at which you measure that altitude. So far we had looked at various examples as if we had been able to stop the movements of the heavens and examine each situation at leisure, but, unlike Joshua, we cannot make the Sun stand still or stay the Moon; all is in continual movement, so that every answer is valid for an infinitesimal period only and we can but try to time it as best we can. The extent of an error in time varies considerably. In the arc-into-time conversion table we see that $1' = 4s$, so that at the worst, an error of 4 seconds could make a difference of one nautical mile; thus a watch misread by a minute could cause an error of 15 miles. It is hardly ever as bad as this, for the heavenly body must be due east or west of you to cause the maximum effect, but a mistake of 1° of LHA (4 minutes) can easily put you 45 miles out.

Do not try at first to take your own time: get someone else to do it for you—and make sure they can tell the time, particularly if they are using an analog watch. It is quite amazing how many people there are who, when you say 'now', do not write down the correct time.

Take your sextant and make yourself comfortable, well supported and firm from the waist down, mobile from the waist up. Make sure that you have a clear view of the Sun and of the horizon below it. Generally, the higher up you are the better, because it is easier to avoid false horizons made by wave tops, but it is not worth making yourself unsteady to gain height. It is also, obviously, important to choose a place where there is a minimum of spray. Arrange your shade glasses so that you have a bright Sun but not one that will dazzle you; use a pale horizon glass to remove glare when necessary.

The clarity of the horizon is of the greatest importance. Sometimes in calms, there is not enough difference between air and water to distinguish the horizon; on other occasions mist obscures the true horizon giving a false horizon closer to you. Very rarely there may be abnormal dip (refraction), which can be recognised by the appearance of 'boiling' on the horizon or by the funnels of distant ships seeming to reach up into the sky. When you have doubts about the reliability of the horizon, if it looks in any way odd or hazy, either avoid sights or treat your results with great caution.

Recording the Sights

When you have the Sun more or less on the horizon, rock the sextant gently from side to side and you will see the Sun swing as if it were attached to a pendulum; it is at the lowest point of this swing that you take the sight. When you feel sure that the Sun is just resting on the horizon, call to your time-keeper and then read off the degrees and minutes from your sextant. How accurately you read your sights depends in part on the sextant: some read to 0'.1, others to 0'.5. Readings to the nearest half minute of arc are quite adequate to start with. Take a series of five sights at about 40-second intervals; they will appear something like the example below.

SUN, Sunday 7 December 1997

Watch			Sextant	
h	m	s		
10	54	31	14°	31.0'
10	55	56	14	32.4
10	56	37	14	36.9
10	57	34	14	33.5
10	58	12	14	38.4
	5)280	170		5)172.2
10	56	34	14°	34.4

You will notice that in this series the Sun is rising, indeed it is still an hour to noon, but it is rising very slowly so that a small error in the observations can make it appear that the Sun is already sinking (look at reading number 4). In spring and autumn the change in altitude will be much more marked. The object of averaging five sights is to compensate for these little mistakes. If you can only take three sights, average them, but do not rely on the position line from a single observation.

Correcting the Data

Now with a watch time of 10h 56m 34s and a sextant altitude of 14°34'.4 you can start to work out your sight. The relevant pages of the *Nautical Almanac* are reproduced as Appendix B.

Watch time to UT (GMT)

	h	m	s	The watch is here assumed to be on UT and 5s fast.
Watch	10	56	34	In other parts of the world, it may be necessary to
Corr.			− 5	allow for zone time.
UT	10	56	29	

Sextant Altitude to True Altitude As we saw earlier, the sextant altitude must be corrected. The first correction is for index error, the error of your sextant (see page 52). In this example an imaginary error of 2'.3 'off' is allowed for. The other corrections are found in the *Nautical Almanac* in the Altitude Correction Tables on the first two pages for the Sun, stars and planets, and at the end for the Moon (see Appendices D and E). Under 'Dip', presuming a height of eye above sea level of between 9 and 10 ft, we find a correction of minus 3'.0. In the Sun column 'Oct-Mar, Lower Limb', against our sextant altitude 14°34' (between 14°18' and 14°42') we find plus 12'.6. This last correction includes both refraction and semi-diameter, so we have:

Sextant	14°	34' .4
IE	+	2 .3
Dip	−	3 .0
Alt. Corr.	+	12 .6
True Alt	14°	46' .3

This is the figure that will be compared with the tabulated altitude.

Note: The Altitude Correction Tables in the *Nautical Almanac* should theoretically be entered with *apparent altitude* (sextant altitude corrected for index error and dip), but this is unnecessarily precise for anything except possibly the Moon, and sextant altitude can be used instead.

Using the Almanac

LHA Sun Each double page in the main body of the *Nautical Almanac* provides the necessary data for three days: on the left, the GHA of Aries, the GHA and declination of Venus, Mars, Jupiter and Saturn, and the Sidereal Hour Angles and declinations of 57 stars; on the right hand, the GHAs and declinations of Sun and Moon and the times of twilight, sunrise and sunset, moonrise and moonset. GHA SUN is tabulated for every hour, and at 10 hours on 7 December 1997 is 332°07′.8, leaving 56m 29s of our chosen UT unaccounted for (Appendix B). The figure to be added to GHA for these minutes and seconds is called the *increment*.

At the back of the *Nautical Almanac* there are a number of yellow pages headed 'Increments and Corrections'. Appendix C shows the page for 56m and 57m. Three columns (Sun/Planets, Aries, Moon) give the, very similar, figures which must be added to the hourly figure of GHA. In the 56m Sun column, against 29s we find 14°07′.3; the increment to be added to GHA SUN for 10h to give GHA SUN at the moment we made our observation, namely 10h 56m 29s. The working looks like this:

GHA SUN (10h)	332°07′.8
Increment (56m 29s)	+ 14 07.3
GHA SUN	346°15′

Now the included angle of the spherical triangle was not GHA but LHA, and when discussing hour angles we saw that LHA equals GHA plus or minus longitude. One way to remember which to do is by the old rhyme:

> Longitude east, GHA least,
> Longitude west, GHA best.

In our case DR longitude is east, so you must add it to get LHA. Personally, I remember the words 'East Add' and write them on any form and any almanac I use. Obviously, west requires the opposite sign.

Using the Tables

Assuming a Position It is necessary at this point to explain the 'assumed position'. In the past the spherical triangle was resolved by the Cosine-

Haversine method and the sight was worked out from the DR position; today it is also easy to use the DR position when working with a computer. Tables, however, cannot print solutions for every minute of arc of latitude, LHA and declination, so the problem is simplified by providing tables only for whole degrees of latitude and LHA. The following three rules determine which position you will assume:

1 Your assumed position must be as near your DR position as possible,
2 Your assumed latitude must be a whole number of degrees,
3 Your assumed longitude must be so arranged as to make your LHA a whole number of degrees.

Rules 1 and 2 are simple and need no explanation; rule 3 is a little more complicated and two imaginary cases are given below:

(a) DR Long E   08° 25′

GHA	337° 01′
Ass Long E	7 59 (E+)
LHA	345° 00′

(b) DR Long W   04° 50′

GHA	27° 32′
Ass Long W	4 32 (E+)
LHA	23° 00′

To return to our sight, DR Longitude is E 001°51′ so to get LHA we have:

GHA	346° 15′.0
Ass Long E	1 45.0 (E+)
LHA	348° 00′.0

As has been said, the assumed latitude must be an integral degree, and since the DR latitude was N51°56′, the assumed latitude will be N52°.

Declination From the same page in the almanac (Appendix B), write down the Sun's declination for 10h (S 22°37′.8) and also note the value of *d* given at the bottom of the column (0′.3). This figure is the difference in declination during one hour; for the Sun a mean figure is tabulated for every three days.

33

Near the solstice the *d* correction is very small. Turning to the '*v* or *d* correction' column on the appropriate page of Increments and Corrections (Appendix C), we see that in this case the correction for 56m (no seconds needed) is also 0′.3. The sign (+or−) for *d* is found by inspection of the declination column: when the declination is increasing, the correction must be added; when decreasing, subtracted. For example, the *d* correction for the Sun will be added from 21 March to 22 June while the declination increases from 0° to N23°, and again from 21 September to 22 December (0° to S23°), but it must be subtracted from 22 June to 21 September (N23° to 0°) and from 22 December to 21 March (S23° to 0°).

It is worth noting that 1 nautical mile is the maximum error that can arise even if the *d* correction for the Sun is ignored altogether.

Tabulated Altitude and Azimuth We have now found the three arguments necessary for entering AP3270: LHA, Declination and Assumed Latitude. In our example:

LHA 348°   Dec S22°38′.1   Ass Lat N52°

In AP3270, Vol 3, turn to Latitude 52° which takes up eight pages with four headings:

    Declination 0°–14°   *same* name as latitude
    Declination 0°–14°   *contrary* name to latitude
    Declination 15°–29°   *same* name as latitude
    Declination 15°–29°   *contrary* name to latitude

'Name' refers to 'north' and 'south' and in our example we must look under *contrary* name because declination is south and latitude north (Appendix F).

Each degree of declination has three columns: the tabulated altitude Hc, the difference *d*, and the azimuth angle Z. (*d* is the difference between the tabulated altitudes of one degree of declination and the next higher degree and determines what proportion of the minutes of declination are to be added or subtracted from Hc.)

Tabular entry should *always* be for the integral degree of declination numerically *less* than (or equal to) the actual declination. The excess over the integral degree, ie the minutes and tenths of minutes of the declination, are called the declination increment. For example, with a declination of 12°50′ the tables will be entered with 12° and the declination increment is 50′.

In our example, declination is 22°38′ (to the nearest minute of arc) so 22° is used as argument and 38′ is the declination increment. Against LHA 348° we read: Hc 15°16′, *d*–60, Z169°. Now this altitude is correct for 22° declination, but is still to be corrected for the declination increment. At the back of

AP3270 (and on a loose card) you will find 'Table 5—Correction to Tabulated Altitude for Minutes of Declination' (Appendix H). Under *d* 60 and against 38 you find 38 again (it will not be the same figure when *d* is not 60). These 38 minutes must now be subtracted (subtracted because *d* was preceded by a minus sign) from 15°16′ to get the correct tabulated altitude:

$$15°16' - 38'.1 = 14°37'.9$$

The last figure from the tables, under Z, is the azimuth angle, and since the Sun has not yet passed your meridian it is N169°E, and the azimuth (Zn) is also 169°. This can be confirmed by the instructions in the top corner of the page of the tables where it states: 'N Lat, LHA greater than 180° ... Z=Zn'.

SUN   Lower/Upper Limb

Date..*7ᵗʰ December 1997*

Watch *10ʰ 56ᴹ 34ˢ*

Corr. _____ *− 5*

UT (*GMT*) *10 56 29*

Dec ♂/S   *22° 37′.8* *d 0:.3*

d ....*0·3*

DECLINATION *− 22 38 (·01)*

DR...*N 51° 56′ E 01° 51′*

GHA ....*332° 07′.8*

Increment ____ *14 07·3*

GHA SUN *346 15 (·1)*

ASS. LONG *E .....1.....45*.........E/W

LHA SUN *348° 00*

ASSUMED LAT *N 52°*

Sextant ......*14° 34′.4*

Index Error *+ 2·3*

Dip ...*− 3·0*

Alt.Corr *+ 12·6*

TRUE ALT *14 46 (·3)*

Hc *15° 16′ d−60.Z169*

d *− 38*

TAB ALT *14 38*

TRUE ALT *14 46*

INTERCEPT *8*

Towards/Away   Zn *169°*

Fig 24

Plotting the Sight

Now the true altitude was 14°46′.3 and the tabulated altitude is less by 8′ or 8 nautical miles. This intercept will be marked 'towards' the Sun because the true altitude is the greater (see Fig 21). Imagine moving towards the Sun; it will get higher and the altitude angle greater. In practice, I advise writing *true altitude greater towards* where you can easily see it and go by rule of thumb.

You are now ready to put the position line on the chart (Fig 25). Mark in the assumed position, draw the azimuth from it (be careful to take it from the true, not the magnetic, rose), mark off 8 miles towards the Sun, draw a line at right angles to the azimuth and there you are!

In case this seems very complicated, Fig 24 shows the workings without explanations: ten small additions or subtractions.

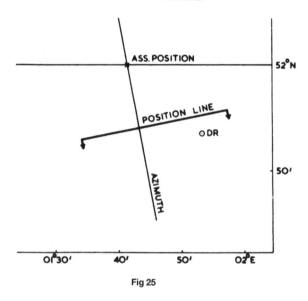

Fig 25

A Sun Sight in Summer

Fig 26 shows another Sun sight taken in July; the relevant pages of the *Nautical Almanac* are reproduced in Appendix A.

You will notice that this second sight varies very little from the first; the assumed longitude is subtracted because 'Longitude west, GHA best'; declination and latitude are both north so we look under 'Declination *same* name as Latitude' in AP3270. Fig 28 shows this sight plotted together with that of the Moon given as an example in the next section.

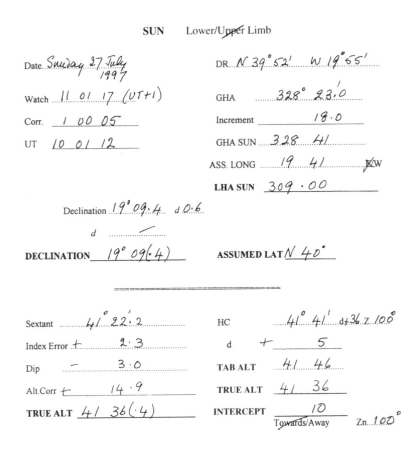

SUN   Lower/Upper Limb

Date.. *Sunday 27 July 1997*

Watch ..*11 01 17 (UT+1)*

Corr. .*1 00 05*

UT .*10 01 12*

DR..*N 39° 52'   W 19° 55'*

GHA .....*328° 23.0*

Increment *18.0*

GHA SUN *328 41*

ASS. LONG ......*19   41*.........W

LHA SUN .*309 · 00*

Declination .*19° 09.4   d 0.6*

d ....

DECLINATION .*19° 09(·4)*   ASSUMED LAT *N 40°*

====================================

Sextant ....*41° 22'·2*

Index Error .+.........*2·3*

Dip .....−.........*3·0*

Alt.Corr +........*14·9*

TRUE ALT .*41 36(·4)*

HC ......*41° 41'*.. d+36 z 100°

d ....+......*5*

TAB ALT .*41   46*

TRUE ALT .*41 36*

INTERCEPT *10*
Towards/Away .... Zn..*100*°

Fig 26

A Moon Sight

Moon sights are as easy to take as Sun sights and almost as easy to work out; they can also be extremely useful. For example, when the Moon is waning and visible in the morning sky, a simultaneous Sun and Moon sight (that is one Sun and one Moon sight taken within a few minutes of each other) gives you two position lines and therefore a fix.

The principle of a Moon sight is exactly the same as that of a Sun sight, but because the Moon moves very irregularly and is much closer to the Earth, the

MOON   Lower/~~Upper~~ Limb

Date _Sunday 27 July 1997_   DR _N 39° 52' W 19° 55'_

UT _09ʰ 47ᴹ 14ˢ_

GHA	39° 11·4	v 9·8	HP 58·1
Increment	11 16·2		
v	7·8		
GHA MOON	50 35·4		
ASS. LONG	19 35·4		
LHA MOON	31° 00·0		ASSUMED LAT N 40°

Dec _N 11° 37·3_   d _+ 8·4_

d _6·7_

DECLINATION _11° 44'_

Sextant	49° 54·3		
IE } Dip }	− ·7		
App. Alt	49 53·6	Hc	50° 06' d+47. Z 128°
1st Corr,	47·0	d	34
2nd Corr	5·4	TAB ALT	50 40
3rd Corr (UL)	(- 30)	TRUE ALT	50 46
True Alt	50 46·0	INTERCEPT	6' Zn 232°
			Towards/~~Away~~

Fig 27

corrections to be applied are more, and more complicated. In the Moon section of the *Nautical Almanac* (Appendix A) five columns for each hour of each day, give:

GHA This is taken out for the hour, and the appropriate increment for minutes and seconds added, as for the Sun.

v The increment for the Moon is tabulated for the lowest rate of change per hour, but the Moon often moves much faster and a correction is necessary for this *variation*.

Dec Declination is tabulated for every hour as for the Sun.

d   The *difference* is given for each hour for the Moon instead of every three days for the Sun. The sign (+ or −) must be found by inspection of the declination, as it was for the Sun.

HP   The correction for horizontal parallax (see page 27) is used for entering the second section of the Altitude Correction Tables for the Moon (Appendix E).

Let us look at an example: if a Moon sight were taken at UT xh 56m 01s and for the day and hour we find the value of v to be 6′.2 and that of d to be 12′.9 then from 'Increments and Corrections' (Appendix C) we get an increment of 13°22′.0, v 5′.8, d 12′.1. The v and d correction columns are valid for the entire minute and no account is to be taken of the seconds of UT. The v correction for the Moon is always additive; the sign for d will depend on the behaviour of the Moon's declination (just as it did for that of the Sun). Neither v nor d can be ignored for the Moon.

Usually you can choose by eye which limb of the Moon to observe, only when it is nearly full is this not so. However, the Almanac does not print the data necessary for a theoretical answer, so go by rule of thumb – waxing upper, waning lower—remembering that, in these rather special circumstances, there may be an error. It is not likely to be more than a mile or so.

Sextant altitude to true altitude is also rather more complicated for the Moon than it was for the Sun. Correct the sextant altitude for index error and dip to arrive at apparent altitude, and with this figure as argument enter the tables at the back of the *Nautical Almanac* (Appendix E). It is superfluous to discuss here the clear instructions given there; here are two examples:

required data	App Alt	33°42′	49°36′
	HP	57′.6	61′.5
	Limb (U or L)	upper	lower
corrections	1st corr	57′.2	47′.2
	2nd corr	3 .6	8 .6
		60 .8	
	Upper Limb	−30 .0	
	Total corr	+ 30′.8	+ 55′.8

In the past the Moon was considered unreliable for observations, probably owing to difficulties with the complicated interpolations that were required for such a fast-moving body. Modern Almanacs made it possible to reduce lunar observations quickly and with all the necessary accuracy.

Fig 27 shows a Moon sight taken a few minutes before the summer Sun sight; the chartwork is shown in Fig 28.

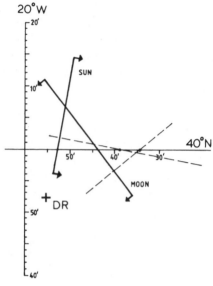

Fig 28

Planet Sights

There is nearly always a planet handy for observing in the early morning or evening. A planet is brighter than a star and can therefore be used when the horizon is more easily visible. Four columns in the *Nautical Almanac* give the data for Venus, Mars, Jupiter and Saturn. Values for *v* and *d* are given at the bottom of each column, each figure being a mean for three days: these corrections are quite small, except for Saturn when an error of (maximum) 2′.7 could be introduced into your calculations by ignoring the corrections. The only difference from Sun and Moon sights is that *v* is sometimes a minus quantity for Venus. The corrections to be applied to sextant altitude are given on pages A2 and A3 of the *Nautical Almanac* (see Appendix D). Index error and dip must be applied as always and the altitude correction is for refraction only, as semi-diameter is not, of course, required.

A diagram in the *Nautical Almanac* displays the movement of the planets throughout the year. Very clear notes on the visibility of each planet and on the use of the diagram allow one to identify each planet, an interesting exercise even when you have no intention of taking a sight. Finally, the notes include a section headed 'Do not confuse' to help when two planets are close together. If, in spite of this, you find that you are sailing briskly through Birmingham, it is quite probable that you have mistaken your planet or even observed a bright star.

Meridian Sights

A meridian sight of the Sun is usually called 'a noon sight' because it is taken at the observer's local noon. When taking a noon sight, the first step is to discover the time the Sun will cross your meridian. the time of the Sun's meridian passage at Greenwich is given for each day at the bottom of the right-hand page of the *Nautical Almanac* (that of the Moon is also given). This time is correct for all points on the Greenwich meridian, but when you are to the east the passage will be earlier and when to the west later. The degrees of your DR longitude must be multiplied by four to get minutes (of time), which must then be added to or subtracted from the time of the meridian passage at Greenwich to give you the UT of the meridian passage on your longitude.

For example, on 6 December 1997 (Appendix B) the meridian passage of the Sun is at 11h 51m. Now at W10° the passage will be (10×4) 40 minutes later, at 12h 31m UT. At E10° the passage will be 40m earlier, at 11h 11m.

The theory of this type of sight was explained on page 20; let us now look at two examples of its working, both from Sun sights 28 July 1997 Sun's Meridian Passage at Greenwich 1206 UT (Appendix A).

DR Latitude N	51° 32′	DR Latitude S	14° 10′	
Longitude	00° 00′	Longitude W	30° 00′	(2 hours)
	90° 00′ .0		90° 00′ .0	
True Altitude	57 05 .6	True Altitude	57 05 .6	
Zenith Distance	32 54 .4		32 54 .4	
Declination N	18 54 .3	Declination N	18 53 .3	
Latitude N	51° 48′ .7	Latitude S	14° 01′ .1	

The Sun appears to remain at the highest point of its trajectory for some time. In our latitudes this varies from about ten minutes in midwinter to four in summer. When it appears on your sextant to have stopped rising, take a series of five sights spread over the next two or three minutes and average them to give your sextant altitude. There is no need to time these sights.

Declination must be taken out for the time of the observation, so that if you are far east or west of the Greenwich meridian the appropriate declination will not be that at 12h UT. In the example above you will see that there are two figures for declination, only slightly different in this case, marking the fact that the second sight is taken in W30°, where noon is two hours later than at Greenwich.

Meridian sights can be taken for any heavenly body, and the times of the meridian passages of the Moon and the planets are given in the *Nautical Almanac* at the foot of the page. The meridian passages of stars are discussed on page 46.

Meridian sights have three advantages: accurate time is not necessary, the working out is very simple, and there is no plotting on the chart.

Star Sights

Sidereal Hour Angle

The GHAs of individual stars are not given in the Almanac. A known point in the heavens, called the First Point of *Aries*, has been chosen and its GHA is tabulated in the Almanac as if it were a heavenly body. The stars, for navigational purposes, are fixed in relation to each other and to *Aries*, so that the

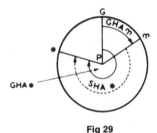

Fig 29

angle at the Pole between the meridian of *Aries* and the meridian of a particular star does not change. This angle, measured in a westerly direction from the meridian of *Aries*, is called Sidereal Hour Angle (SHA). The SHA and declination of 57 selected stars are listed in the *Nautical Almanac* every three days. In Fig 29 we see:

GHA *Aries*:   The hour angle of the meridian of *Aries* measured westwards from the Greenwich meridian.

SHA Star: The hour angle of the star measured westwards from the meridian of *Aries*. This angle does not alter.

GHA Star: The hour angle of the star measured westwards from the Greenwich meridian.

This last angle *always* equals the sum of the other two hour angles:

$$\text{GHA } Aries + \text{SHA Star} = \text{GHA Star}$$

Let us look at an example. On 8 December 1997, DR position N35°43′, E19°12′, *Sirius* is observed at 04h 56m 32s:

GHA *Aries* (04h)	136° 57′ .2	(Appendix B)
Increment (56m 32s)	14 10 .3	(Appendix C)
GHA *Aries*	151 07 .5	
SHA *Sirius*	258 43 .9	(Appendix B)
	409 51 .4	
	− 360	
GHA *Sirius*	49° 51′ .4	

Dealing with hour angles, when an addition comes to more than 360° that figure is subtracted. (Likewise if a minus quantity appears, 360° are added.) The increment to be added to GHA *Aries* for the minutes and seconds of GMT is found in the *Aries* column on the 'Increments and Corrections' page. Having found GHA Star, LHA Star is obtained in the normal way by adding or subtracting longitude.

Declinations

The declinations of stars virtually do not change during the year. They are printed, together with SHA, in the Star column in the main body of the Almanac. Provided the declination of a star is less than 30° (north or south) the sight can be worked out from Vols 2 and 3 of AP3270 as for other heavenly bodies. Concise Sight Reduction Tables (see page 55) can be used for declinations of more than 30°. AP3270 Vol 1 is designed specifically for star sights, however, and is more convenient because it tells you which star to use when, and where it is.

Twilight and the Preparation of Star Sights

On the right-hand pages of the *Nautical Almanac* times are given for the beginning (am) and end (pm) of civil and nautical twilight as well as the rising and setting times of the Sun and Moon. The figures in these tables are correct for the middle day on each page and for every 10° of latitude. When great accuracy is required, interpolation is necessary for the first and third days and for the other latitudes. Civil twilight lasts from the time the Sun disappears until it is 6° below the horizon (and vice versa in the morning), and is when the brightest stars are visible and there is a clear horizon: later and the horizon will have disappeared. The length of civil twilight varies from about half an hour at the equator to over one hour in the far north or south: you will plan your sights accordingly. An approximate time for starting the observations is adequate, but make sure you start early enough if you are not to struggle on deck, sextant in hand, only to find that the horizon has merged into night.

Let us look at an example of planning, first with individual stars (using AP3270 Vols 2 and 3) and then with the stars selected by Vol 1. We can work to the nearest degree.

Evening 28 July 1997, DR position N35° W40°

Civil twilight ends at Greenwich	19h 59m	
Longitude (40°) × 4	2 40	15°= 1 hour
Civil twilight ends at W 40°	22h 39m UT	

To make the most of the short half hour the stars will be available, you will need to be on deck soon after sunset at about 22h 20m UT. (This may be 20h 20m your time, depending in which time zone you have placed yourself.)

You may recognise them, but it is not easy to pick up a star in sextant. The approximate altitude should be set on the instrument, then, looking along the azimuth, the star will appear more or less on the horizon. The easiest way to do this is to plan with the help of AP3270, Vol 1 Selected Stars.

GHA *Aries* (22h)	276° 36′.1
Increment (39m)	9 46 .6
	286 (22.7) ignore minutes
Long W (E add)	−40
LHA *Aries*	246°

In AP3270 Vol 2, page LAT 35°N and argument LHA *Aries* 246, we find the tabulated altitude (Hc) and azimuth (Zn) of the seven best stars for observing at that time on that latitude. Capitals tell us that the star is bright (magnitude greater than 1.5) while asterisks identify the three stars most suitable for a three-line fix. Notice how the azimuths start in the north east and veer round to north west.

DENEB*	ALTAIR	Nunki	ANTARES*
41° 06′ 057°	36° 12′ 106°	19° 04′ 145°	28° 34′ 179°

SPICA	ARCTURUS	Alkaid*
27° 23′ 231°	57° 32′ 249°	58° 06′ 309°

Selected Stars

Vol 1 of AP3270 gives seven advantageous stars to observe for each degree of latitude and of LHA *Aries*. Instead of the azimuth angle (Z), azimuth (Zn) is given direct; this is possible because solutions for north and south latitudes are tabulated separately. One last example (Fig 30 and Appendix G), in the southern hemisphere, gives the entire working for a series of morning observations and shows how simple the calculation is. For planning, each star has been given 1° of LHA later than the preceding one to allow for the passage of time. This takes almost half an hour and brings us to sunrise, which is at 04h 13m, ship's time, at our longitude. Be ready to take your sights at 0340, starting just as soon as you can see a decent horizon and with a bit of luck finishing before the Sun makes the stars invisible. Take at least three sights of each star, and average them and correct for index error and dip to obtain true altitude. The working done, these sights can now be plotted on the chart, a long and tedious business needing care and accuracy: a degree wrong in plotting an azimuth makes a sizable error when there is a big intercept. The most probable position is now chosen and this is discussed on page 48.

In the example chosen, all seven are first magnitude stars. A check with the planets will show that only *Jupiter* is available at that time, almost due north with an altitude of about 32°. Were more position lines needed, *Jupiter* would do well. In practice, by the time you achieve all seven stars and one planet in the half hour available to you, you will be an expert.

There is no doubt that, particularly in a series of star sights, a calculator has a lot to offer because you can work from your DR position which makes for much easier plotting; and, if the intercepts are small, you will immediately be encouraged by the accuracy of your sights, and of your DR.

Precession and Nutation

Vol 1 of AP3270 has to be renewed every nine years or so because, entering direct from LHA *Aries*, no account can be taken of precession and nutation. (These are two wobbles: precession is a slow eastward movement of the equinoctial points along the ecliptic, while nutation is a fluctuation in the precessional movement of the Earth's pole about the pole of the ecliptic.) A correction for these two is given in two places, Table 5 at the back of Vol 1, and on a loose sheet (the first for aircraft, the second, more accurate, for ships) using as arguments the year, LHA *Aries* and the latitude. In the example here the final fix has to be moved 0.1nm, 120°. This correction applies *only* to a position line or fix deduced from AP3270 Vol 1. When *Polaris* or a planet has been observed with the other stars, the position lines must not be transferred; and in such a case, each star position line should be moved individually before using all the sights to arrive at a fix.

Stars with AP3270 (HO249) Vol 1 Epoch 1995.0
PLANNING

DATE **7th December '97**　　　　　　DR **S40°, E153°**

STANDARD TIME **UT + 10h**

CIVIL TWILIGHT BEGINS	03h 52m	GHA Aries	331° 12'·3
LONG.*153°* × 4 MINS	− 10 12	INCREMENT	10 01·6
CIVIL TWILT BEGINS UT	17 40	GHA Aries	341 13·9
SHIP'S TIME	03 40	ASS. LONG.	152 46·1 (E+)
		LHA Aries	134°

STAR	*REGULUS	SPICA	*ACRUX	CANOPUS	*RIGEL	BETELGEUSE	PROCYON
LHA	135°	136°	137°	138°	139°	140°	141°
Hc	35°39'	26°05'	52°59'	58°52'	27°44'	23°04'	38°4·'
Zn	021°	082°	145°	232°	283°	303°	326°

PLANNING

	REGULUS	*SPICA	ACRUX	*CANOPUS	RIGEL	BETELGEUSE	*PROCYON
LHA	135°	136°	137°	138°	139'	140°	141'
Hc	35°39	26°03	52°57	58°53	27°46	23°06	38°43
Zn	021°	083°	145°	232°	283°	303°	326°

SIGHTS

	REGULUS	*SPICA	ACRUX	*CANOPUS	RIGEL	BETELGEUSE	*PROCYON
Watch 8/12	03 44 15	03 48 01	03 51 37	03 55 08	03 57 45	04 01 36	04 04 23
UT 7/12	17 44 10	17 47 56	17 51 32	17 55 03	17 57 40	18 01 31	18 04 18
GHA Aries	331°30'·1	331°30'·1	331°30'·1	331°30'·1	330°30·1	346°22'·5	346°32'·5
Increment	11 04·3	12 01·1	12 55·1	13 48·1	14 27·4	20·3	1 04·7
GHA Aries	342 34·4	343 31·2	344 25·2	345 18·1	345 57·5	346 52·8	347 37·2
Ass.Long	153 25·6	153 28·8	152 34·8	152 21·9	153 02·5	153 07·2	153 22·8
LHA Aries	496°/136°	497°/137°	497°/137°	498°/138°	498°/139°	500°/140°	501°/141°
Hc	35°38	26°48	52°57	58°53	27°46	23°06	38°43
Ho	36° 14	27° 04	52°47	58° 30	27°44	22°51	38°44
Intercept	19 T	16 T	10 A	23 A	2 A	15 A	1 T
Zn	019°	082°	145°	232°	283°	303°	326

December 1997 Tasman Sea 40S 153E (Local time UT+10)

Fig 30 (plotted in Fig. 35)

Using the Meridian Passage

Each star crosses the observer's meridian when LHA *Aries* = 360° − SHA
Star. To find the time of a given LHA *Aries* the observer's longitude must be
added (W) or subtracted from (E) LHA to get GHA; the time (UT) of this
GHA is then found in the Almanac. For example, to find the time of the
meridian passage of *Sirius* in Long W10° on 7 December 1997:

SHA Sirius 258°43′.9

360°–258°43′.9	=101°16′.1=LHA *Aries*
101°16′.1+10° (Long W)	=111°16′.1=GHA *Aries*
GHA *Aries* at 02h	=105°53′.1
difference	5°23′.0

By inspecting the Almanac, we find that at 02h, GHA *Aries* is 105°53′.1 and that 5°23′ is the increment for 21m 29s, giving a meridian passage of *Sirius* at 02h 21m 29s UT.

(Pole Star Sights) *Polaris*

As has already been said, if *Polaris* were directly over the North Pole its true altitude would be the latitude of the observer; but *Polaris* can bear up to 2° east or west of true north, so a correction is necessary.

When you take your sight of *Polaris*, notice the time—the nearest minute will do. Let us say that your sight was at about 03h 15m UT on 28 July 1997; DR N52°50′, E03°42′. The sextant altitude (preferably three averaged readings) is corrected as for a star or planet (index error and dip followed by refraction from the Altitude Correction Tables (Appendix D)) to give true altitude.

From the Almanac now find the appropriate GHA *Aries* and correct it for longitude to arrive at LHA *Aries*. Turning to the *Polaris* tables in the *Nautical Almanac* three correction tables (a_0, a_1, a_2) are found on the same page and are entered with arguments LHA, latitude and month. The three corrections, all taken from the same column determined by LHA, are then added, always, to True Alt and 1° subtracted to arrive at Latitude. It takes longer to describe than to work.

GHA *Aries* (03h)	350°49′.3	True Alt	53°14′.0
Increment (15m)	3 45 .6	a_0 (358° 17′)	+24′.2
DR Long. E	3 42 .0 (E+)	a_1 (Lat.53)	+ .6
LHA *Aries*	358° 16′.9	a_2 (July)	+ .3
		−1°	−1°00′.0
		LAT	52°39′.1

Selecting the Best Position

'The mark of a good navigator is not so much his ability to obtain accurate information as his ability to evaluate and interpret correctly the information available to him', said Captain Alton B Moody, USNR. We must now make sure that having taken, calculated and plotted our sight, we know how to use it. An experienced observer, taking a series of sights in good conditions, should finish with a possible position line error of 0.5nm. This means that there is a band, 1 mile wide, in which the ship lies. Fig 31 shows how the area

Fig 31

of uncertainty from the DR plot is reduced by a single position line. With two position lines the position is defined, given equal confidence in either line, by their point of intersection. With three it is generally taken to be at the centre of the cocked hat, although when there is, for example, a systematic error (as from an index or dip error) the position could in fact lie outside it. This is shown in Fig 32 where a systematic error has moved each position line away

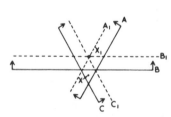

Fig 32 Three position lines, A,B,C, each with a constant error give the apparent position of the ship at X. A_1,B_1,C_1, the same position lines without the constant error, show the ship to have been in fact at X_1.

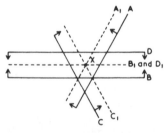

Fig 33 Position-line D enables the constant error to be recognised and allowed for; both sets of position lines, ABCD (with constant error), and A_1,B_1,C_1,D_1 (without constant error), show the ship's position to be at X.

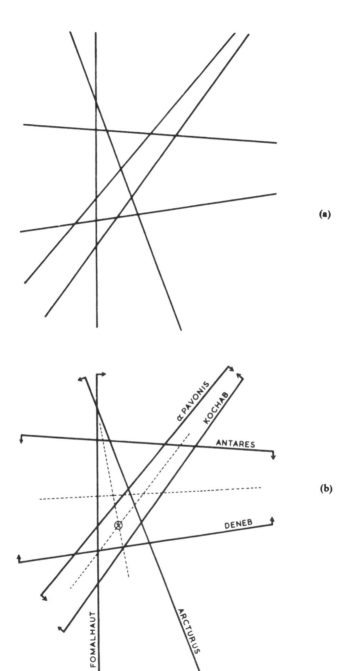

(a)

(b)

Fig 34

from the direction of the bodies observed as shown by the 'azimuth' arrows.

The surest way to evaluate plots is to draw azimuth arrows on each line and to bisect the angle between those which point away from or towards each other; the intersection of these bisectors will then define the position. However, the bisector method is only reliable when the difference in azimuth is greater than 60°. Looking again at Fig 32 we see that the azimuths were 311°, 000° and 036°. there being a 60° difference only between the first and last. Fig 33 shows how a fourth position line (with the same systematic error) with an azimuth of 180° clarifies the situation.

It should be noted that the cocked hat in Fig 32 was not only unreliable because of the bad distribution of azimuth but also suspect because the arrows in lines A and C point in towards the cocked hat while those on B point away: in a truly reliable series of sights the arrows should either all point out from the enclosed area or all point in towards it as in Fig 33. When

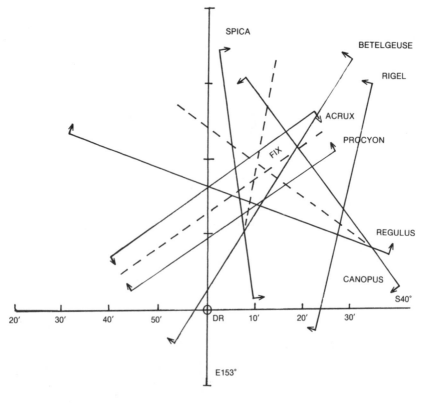

Fig 35

some arrows point in and others out, there is an inconsistency which should be resolved before trusting too much to the position obtained.

With several lines, say from six star sights, there will be more evidence but the plot will also be more difficult to interpret. Fig 34a shows a real series of six star sights which at first seem most difficult to resolve, there being several cocked hats and enclosed areas. Fig 34b shows the same sights with azimuth arrows and the bisectors of the pairs of position lines most widely separated in azimuth: it is now clear that there was an equal systematic error of five of the lines round the most probable position and that only one (*Antares*) has a considerably larger error. Fig 35 plots our imaginary star sight from page 46, and we can see from the direction of the arrows (all inwards) that the position lines are consistent. *Rigel* is of little help, but the bisectors between the three pairs *Regulus* and *Canopus*, *Spica* and *Betelgeuse*, *Acrux* and *Procyon*, are quite adequate to find a reliable position.

In general the position can usually be deduced to sufficient accuracy by taking the centre of the area enclosing the largest number of intersections. As with terrestrial bearings, the prudent navigator will adopt the position nearest danger, for example, land.

Those who wish to pursue the subject further should read the *Journal of Navigation*, Vol 15, No 3, page 341, where Michael Richey writes on interpreting astro position lines at sea. He gives the references for a number of articles on the subject, particularly 'The use of bisectors in selecting the most probable position' by M Bini in the same *Journal*, Vol 8, page 195.

Notes

Sextants

A sextant is so called because the arc at the bottom is one-sixth of a circle (60°). However, it measures 120° because moving the index arm 1° moves the image of the Sun by 2°. The attractive, but seldom seen, octant is based on one-eighth of a circle and measures 90°: smaller and easier to stow than a sextant, it is quite adequate for normal navigational purposes. The principles of a sextant and an octant are the same and we can call them all sextants for convenience.

When you look through the eyepiece of your sextant you see part of a rectangular frame. The left-hand side is plain glass through which you can see the horizon, the right-hand side of this is a mirror which reflects the light from another mirror which is fixed to the top of the sextant and swings with the index arm. The bottom of the index arm swings along a scale calibrated in degrees. The minutes of arc are read off the wheel by which the small adjustments are made. In older sextants, minutes are (with difficulty) read off the degree scale with the help of a vernier.

Cover the top mirror with one or two of the tinted shades, then face the Sun and look through the eyepiece at the horizon (or the garden fence) underneath the Sun. Move the index arm very slowly until the Sun appears, then with the small adjuster wheel 'move' the Sun until it rests on the horizon. This is your sight. Read your sextant to the nearest half minute: the result is your sextant altitude.

Sextants are delicate instruments and must be treated carefully. Various errors can occur of which the chief are listed below.

Sextant Error This is the basic error of the instrument and should be marked by the manufacturer in the lid of the box. It should be negligible.

Index Error A variable error that should be checked fairly frequently. Set the sextant roughly at zero and look at the Sun (do not forget the shades). You will see two suns: bring them so that their edges are just touching and read the sextant, then reverse the suns and read it again. You will find that one reading will be the ordinary scale (on) and one on the minus side (off). Subtract the smaller from the larger, halve it, and the result is the index error, to be added when the greater number is 'off', and subtracted when 'on'. You can test the accuracy of your reading by adding the two figures: the sum should equal four times the semi-diameter of the Sun. The sum might look like this:

17 July 1990, SD 15'8 (from bottom of Sun column in Almanac)

Sextant readings 33'.2 on	check 33'.2
30 .0 off	30 .0
2) 3 .2	4)63 .2
Index error 1'.6 on	15'.8

Taken to the nearest half minute, the index error is 1'.5 'on', and this must be subtracted from the sextant altitude.

There is another, less accurate but quicker, way of checking the index error on a really clear day. Set your sextant at zero and you will see two horizons. Turn the wheel until these form one straight line when the reading should, but will probably not, be zero: the difference is the index error. The Admiralty *Manual of Navigation* advises that sextants should be adjusted when the index error is greater than 3'.

Imaginary index errors are used in the examples in this book.

Side error When you check the index error by the first system, the two suns should appear precisely over each other. When they are very much out of alignment the sextant should be adjusted.

There are other sextant errors and these, together with methods of adjustment, can be found in the Admiralty *Manual of Navigation* Vol 1.

Spherical Triangles

The basic formulae for finding the size of an angle or the length of side of a spherical triangle are given in Fig 36.

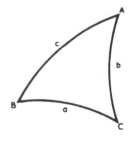

$$\cos a = \cos b \cos c + \sin b \sin c \cos A$$

$$\cos C = \frac{\cos c - \cos a \cos b}{\sin a \sin b}$$

Fig 36

Calculators

Specialised navigational calculators or calculators with navigational software take what little hard work there is left out of astro. However, before you rush off to buy one, try out a friend's to make sure this is really worth while adding such an expensive item to your equipment. Remember that you will never be able to dispense entirely with your almanac and tables because all batteries can run down and electronic gear is not a lover of salt water.

Let us look at what a calculator can do. Sextants exist that average sight and time as you take the sights. Otherwise you must take the sights and time them. The previously tiresome and error-prone averaging is a few seconds' work for programmes that use minutes and seconds of arc as easily as decimals.

The calculator's main function is to resolve the spherical triangle which, we have seen, lies behind every sight. The old Cosine-Haversine method of working out sights used the ship's DR for the observer's position (Z in Fig 19). The great disadvantage of sight reduction tables is that the observer must be assumed to be at position chosen to suit the tables, a choice that sometimes makes plotting awkward. Using a calculator, the DR position can, once again, be the starting point for our chartwork.

There are many other navigational uses to which calculators can be put. Apart from practical use, a calculator with trigonometric functions makes for easy understanding of navigational problems. The *Nautical Almanac* includes a section entitled 'Sight Reduction Procedures, methods and formulae for direct computation' which gives a number of examples. Those with a mathematical ability should be able to resolve the following equations without too much difficulty. The calculator combined with *Reeds Astro Navigation Tables* removes the need for much tedious calculation; the book includes the relevant formulae.

(i) sin Tab Alt = sin Lat sin Dec + cos Lat cos Dec cos LHA

In this formula, which supplies the tabulated altitude, as in others, declinations may be positive or negative; when *same* name as Lat (both S or both N) it is positive, when *opposite* name negative.

(ii) $$\cos \text{azimuth angle} = \frac{\sin \text{Dec} - \sin \text{Tab Alt} \sin \text{Lat}}{\cos \text{Tab Alt} \cos \text{Lat}}$$

(iii) cos great circle distance =
$$\sin \text{Lat}_1 \sin \text{Lat}_2 + \cos \text{Lat}_1 \cos \text{Lat}_2 \cos \text{diff Long}$$

Formula (iii) is identical to formula (i) and gives the distance between, say, Bermuda and Bishop Rock Light. The answer will appear as degrees and minutes, so the degrees must be multiplied by 60 to reduce them to nautical miles.

How much longer would the rhumb line course be than that of the great circle? The length of the rhumb line course is found by:

(iv)
$$\frac{60 \text{ diff Lat}}{\cos \text{ rhumb line course}}$$

It may appear as a minus figure, but ignore the sign.

If you want to know the declination of a rising or setting body, then:

(v) $$\sin \text{ Dec} \doteq \cos \text{ Lat } \cos \text{ azimuth}$$

but be careful of the refraction.

The rhumb line course, and it may not be easy to measure it from the chart, is given by:

(vi) $$\tan C = \frac{\pi(\text{Long}_1 - \text{Long}_2)}{180 \,[\ln \tan(-5 + \frac{1}{2}\text{Lat}_2) - \ln \tan(45 + \frac{1}{2}\text{Lat}_1)]}$$

where C is the rhumb line, course and 1 and 2 are the latitude and longitude of the two ends (eg Bermuda and the Bishop Rock Light). This formula looks awful, but starting at the bottom right and working backwards it is really quite easy.

The azimuth of any body at its rising or setting (when ZD = 90°) permits you to check your compass and can be found by:

(vii) $$\cos \text{ azimuth} = \frac{\sin \text{ Dec}}{\cos \text{ Lat}}$$

(viii) $$\cos \text{ Lat, or } 1/\cos \text{ Lat (secant)}$$

provides the ratio for a Mercator projection without tables (see Plotting Sheets, below).

At the push of a button or two, a specialised navigational calculator offers an almanac for several decades for at least the Sun and Aries, the various answers to all the formulae above, altitude corrections, noon sights, course and speed made good, workings in arc or time, and a host of other possibilities. My NC77 adds, unsurprisingly, to the speed and accuracy of any work, but I find it also adds amazingly to my interest in the subject—perhaps because, among other reasons, it removes the constant nagging doubt as to whether I have done the last addition correctly.

Concise Sight Reduction Tables

There is no need today to carry separate books of tables with you at all. The *Nautical Almanac* carries 32 pages of figures, the Concise Sight Reduction Tables, which will solve your triangles for you. These tables have not been used for the reduction of sights in the text of this book because the procedure is considerably more complicated: unnecessarily so for a beginner. *Reeds Astro Navigation Tables*, which for many years was an integral part of *Reeds Nautical Almanac*, is now published annually as a stand-alone volume.

'In many circumstances, the accuracy provided by these tables is sufficient. However, to maintain the full accuracy (0′.1) of the ephemeral data in the Almanac throughout their reduction to altitude and azimuth, more extensive tables or calculators should be used.' This quotation from the introduction to these new tables need not to worry us overmuch because we have already compromised the accuracy of the *Nautical Almanac* by using it in conjunction with AP3270 rather than with NP401. However, accuracy apart, and certainly the accuracy is adequate for most yacht navigation, the procedure is more liable to human error. I, for one, find that it needs care to get the right sign (+ or −) and one must remember that A, F and P are taken to the nearest degree, unlike other tables. But those who practise will soon learn, and the convenience is undeniable.

Here is our sight of 7 December worked with the Concise Tables.

Lat 52° LHA 348°   Dec − 22°38′
Reduction table, 1st entry
  (Lat, LHA) = (52,348)   A=   7° 21   A°=7,   A′= 21
                              B= +37 23   Z$_1$= +80.5
                              Dec= −22 38
                              F=   14 45   F°= 15,   F′= 45
Reduction table, 2nd entry
  (A°, F°) = (7,15)   H=   14 53   P°= 83,   Z$_2$= +88.1

Aux table, 1st entry   −15
  (F′, P°)=(45,83)   14 38   Z$_1$= +80.5

Aux Table, 2nd entry   −1   Z$_2$= +88.1
(A′, Z2)=(21,88)   HC   14° 38   Z= 168.6=Zn

This tabulated altitude 14°37′ is to be compared with that using AP3270, which was 14°38′. The azimuths are 168.6° and 169° so in these sights there is little to choose between the systems.

Practice Sights

Useful experience can be gained at home finding the whereabouts of your house with an artificial horizon. This is a horizontal reflecting surface which enables you to measure with your sextant the angle between the heavenly body and its reflection; the angle is double the altitude of the Sun.

The simplest form of artificial horizon is water in a bucket, but unless it is covered with oil it can only be used in very calm weather or the ripples distort the reflection. Ideally, a shallow bowl of mercury or oil is used which gives a better and steadier reflection.

On a windless sunny day, place yourself in line with the Sun and the bucket and with the sextant bring the 'real' Sun down to its reflection. Superimpose the two suns and take a series of five sights, about one a minute, timing them carefully. Average these observations and then halve the resulting angle to obtain sextant altitude. Corrections for dip and semi-diameter are not needed, but those for index error and refraction must be applied to arrive at true altitude. The Altitude Correction Table for Stars and Planets (Appendix D) can be used as a simple refraction table. A sight of the Moon is easy to take and is less dazzling than the Sun. Use the instructions given in the Moon Altitude Correction Tables (Appendix E) for bubble sextants for correcting the sextant altitude.

If your position line does not pass directly through your house you may have made a mistake in the sight or you may not know where you live and have placed your house incorrectly on the plotting sheet.

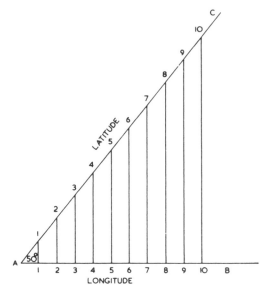

Fig 37

57

Plotting Sheets

There are occasions when the chart is not suitable for plotting observations. Practising on land, the chart may not cover your area; far out to sea, the chart may not be of a scale to permit accurate plotting of a series of sights, or even if it is, the resulting mass of lines might make it almost unusable. Mercator plotting sheets are published and sold by Imrays to meet these problems. Each sheet covers 3° of latitude with a scale of 1:670,000. However it is simple to make your own plotting sheet – and cheaper; you need to know only the

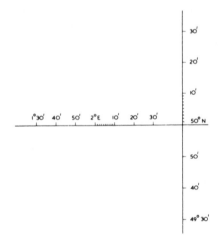

Fig 38

correct proportion, the Lat:Long ratio, at your chosen latitude. The ratio can be found geometrically, or mathematically by tables or calculator.

Fig 37 shows how to find this ratio geometrically. Angle A is drawn the size of the required latitude (here, 50°); convenient units of longitude are marked along AC (say 10mm = 20nm) and the perpendiculars drawn to AB. AB has now been divided into units proportional to the degree of latitude chosen. Great accuracy is required: an error of 1° in low latitudes will cause little distortion, but any inaccuracy in high latitudes will be directly reflected in the plotted position.

Using a calculator, or tables, find cos Lat. For instance, cos 50 = 0.643, then using scale 10mm to 1nm you will represent 1 minute of arc of longitude (at latitude 50° only) by 6.43mm. On the other hand, if you want units of longitude to be 1, then the ratio Long:Lat is given by the secant (1/cos). Sec

50 is 1.556, so if 1 minute of arc of longitude is to be 10mm then 1' Lat (or 1nm) will be 15.56mm. Remember that in Mercator's projection, while meridians are equi-distant from the equator to the poles, the distance between the parallels of latitude get further and further apart. Except at the Equator, 1° Lat is always longer (on the chart) than 1° Longitude, and double at 60°N and S.

Fig 38 shows a home-made plotting sheet for use at latitude 50° (N or S) and any required longitude (here shown between 1°30' and 2°30'E). The steady change in the Lat:Long ratio from the equator to the poles makes it inadvisable for a home-made sheet to cover more than 1° of latitude. 30' north and south of a whole degree allows all the plotting for one assumed degree of latitude. If a greater range is required a new sheet should be made. Except for the limited area described, reliance should not be placed on home-made plotting sheets as gross errors may result.

Appendix A

1997 JULY 27, 28, 29 (SUN., MON., TUES.)

UT	ARIES	VENUS −3.9		MARS +0.8		JUPITER −2.8		SATURN +0.6		STARS		
d h	GHA	GHA	Dec	GHA	Dec	GHA	Dec	GHA	Dec	Name	SHA	Dec
27 00	304 42.8	148 07.7	N11 22.3	107 11.3	S 7 47.5	343 15.0	S16 06.1	284 58.7	N 5 35.9	Acamar	315 27.6	S40 18.7
01	319 45.2	163 07.3	21.2	122 12.5	48.1	358 17.8	06.2	300 01.1	35.9	Achernar	335 35.8	S57 14.7
02	334 47.7	178 06.9	20.1	137 13.6	48.6	13 20.5	06.3	315 03.5 ·	35.9	Acrux	173 23.1	S63 05.3
03	349 50.1	193 06.6 ..	18.9	152 14.8 ..	49.2	28 23.3 ..	06.4	330 06.0 ..	35.9	Adhara	255 22.4	S28 58.1
04	4 52.6	208 06.2	17.8	167 15.9	49.8	43 26.1	06.5	345 08.4	35.9	Aldebaran	291 03.5	N16 30.1
05	19 55.1	223 05.8	16.6	182 17.1	50.4	58 28.8	06.6	0 10.9	35.9			
06	34 57.5	238 05.4	N11 15.5	197 18.2	S 7 50.9	73 31.6	S16 06.7	15 13.3	N 5 35.9	Alioth	166 31.6	N55 58.7
07	50 00.0	253 05.1	14.3	212 19.4	51.5	88 34.3	06.8	30 15.7	35.9	Alkaid	153 08.6	N49 19.9
08	65 02.5	268 04.7	13.2	227 20.5	52.1	103 37.1	06.9	45 18.2	35.9	Al Na'ir	27 58.5	S46 58.1
S 09	80 04.9	283 04.3	12.0	242 21.7 ..	52.7	118 39.9 ..	07.0	60 20.6 ..	35.9	Alnilam	275 58.9	S 1 12.3
U 10	95 07.4	298 04.0	10.9	257 22.8	53.2	133 42.6	07.1	75 23.0	35.9	Alphard	218 08.3	S 8 38.9
N 11	110 09.9	313 03.6	09.7	272 24.0	53.8	148 45.4	07.2	90 25.5	35.9			
D 12	125 12.3	328 03.2	N11 08.6	287 25.1	S 7 54.4	163 48.2	S16 07.3	105 27.9	N 5 35.9	Alphecca	126 21.2	N26 43.7
A 13	140 14.8	343 02.9	07.4	302 26.3	55.0	178 50.9	07.4	120 30.4	35.9	Alpheratz	357 55.8	N29 04.5
Y 14	155 17.3	358 02.5	06.3	317 27.4	55.5	193 53.7	07.5	135 32.8	35.9	Altair	62 19.7	N 8 51.9
15	170 19.7	13 02.1 ..	05.1	332 28.6 ..	56.1	208 56.5 ..	07.6	150 35.2 ..	35.9	Ankaa	353 27.5	S42 18.9
16	185 22.2	28 01.8	04.0	347 29.7	56.7	223 59.2	07.7	165 37.7	35.9	Antares	112 40.9	S26 25.5
17	200 24.6	43 01.4	02.8	2 30.9	57.3	239 02.0	07.8	180 40.1	35.9			
18	215 27.1	58 01.0	N11 01.7	17 32.0	S 7 57.8	254 04.8	S16 07.9	195 42.6	N 5 35.8	Arcturus	146 06.8	N19 12.0
19	230 29.6	73 00.7	11 00.5	32 33.2	58.4	269 07.5	08.0	210 45.0	35.8	Atria	107 53.3	S69 01.5
20	245 32.0	88 00.3	10 59.4	47 34.3	59.0	284 10.3	08.1	225 47.4	35.8	Avior	234 23.5	S59 30.2
21	260 34.5	103 00.0 ..	58.2	62 35.5	7 59.6	299 13.0 ..	08.2	240 49.9 ..	35.8	Bellatrix	278 45.3	N 6 20.8
22	275 37.0	117 59.6	57.0	77 36.6	8 00.2	314 15.8	08.3	255 52.3	35.8	Betelgeuse	271 14.7	N 7 24.3
23	290 39.4	132 59.2	55.9	92 37.7	00.7	329 18.6	08.4	270 54.8	35.8			
28 00	305 41.9	147 58.9	N10 54.7	107 38.9	S 8 01.3	344 21.3	S16 08.5	285 57.2	N 5 35.8	Canopus	264 02.0	S52 41.6
01	320 44.4	162 58.5	53.6	122 40.0	01.9	359 24.1	08.6	300 59.6	35.8	Capella	280 52.7	N45 59.5
02	335 46.8	177 58.1	52.4	137 41.2	02.5	14 26.9	08.7	316 02.1	35.8	Deneb	49 39.2	N45 16.4
03	350 49.3	192 57.8	51.3	152 42.3 ..	03.0	29 29.6	08.8	331 04.5 ..	35.8	Denebola	182 46.2	N14 35.3
04	5 51.8	207 57.4	50.1	167 43.5	03.6	44 32.4	08.9	346 07.0	35.8	Diphda	349 07.9	S17 59.9
05	20 54.2	222 57.1	48.9	182 44.6	04.2	59 35.2	09.0	1 09.4	35.8			
06	35 56.7	237 56.7	N10 47.8	197 45.7	S 8 04.8	74 37.9	S16 09.1	16 11.8	N 5 35.8	Dubhe	194 07.1	N61 46.0
07	50 59.1	252 56.3	46.6	212 46.9	05.3	89 40.7	09.2	31 14.3	35.8	Elnath	278 28.2	N28 36.1
08	66 01.6	267 56.0	45.5	227 48.0	05.9	104 43.5	09.3	46 16.7	35.8	Eltanin	90 51.3	N51 29.7
M 09	81 04.1	282 55.6 ..	44.3	242 49.2	06.5	119 46.2	09.4	61 19.2 ..	35.8	Enif	33 58.7	N 9 52.0
O 10	96 06.5	297 55.3	43.1	257 50.3	07.1	134 49.0	09.5	76 21.6	35.8	Fomalhaut	15 37.1	S29 37.9
N 11	111 09.0	312 54.9	42.0	272 51.4	07.7	149 51.8	09.6	91 24.1	35.8			
D 12	126 11.5	327 54.6	N10 40.8	287 52.6	S 8 08.2	164 54.5	S16 09.8	106 26.5	N 5 35.8	Gacrux	172 14.6	S57 06.2
A 13	141 13.9	342 54.2	39.7	302 53.7	08.8	179 57.3	09.9	121 28.9	35.8	Gienah	176 04.9	S17 31.7
Y 14	156 16.4	357 53.8	38.5	317 54.9	09.4	195 00.1	10.0	136 31.4	35.8	Hadar	149 05.1	S60 21.8
15	171 18.9	12 53.5 ..	37.3	332 56.0 ..	10.0	210 02.8 ..	10.1	151 33.8 ..	35.8	Hamal	328 14.4	N23 26.9
16	186 21.3	27 53.1	36.2	347 57.1	10.5	225 05.6	10.2	166 36.3	35.8	Kaus Aust.	83 59.5	S34 23.0
17	201 23.8	42 52.8	35.0	2 58.3	11.1	240 08.4	10.3	181 38.7	35.8			
18	216 26.2	57 52.4	N10 33.8	17 59.4	S 8 11.7	255 11.1	S16 10.4	196 41.2	N 5 35.8	Kochab	137 19.6	N74 10.4
19	231 28.7	72 52.1	32.7	33 00.6	12.3	270 13.9	10.5	211 43.6	35.8	Markab	13 50.1	N15 11.6
20	246 31.2	87 51.7	31.5	48 01.7	12.8	285 16.7	10.6	226 46.0	35.8	Menkar	314 27.8	N 4 04.8
21	261 33.6	102 51.4 ..	30.3	63 02.8 ..	13.4	300 19.5 ..	10.7	241 48.5 ..	35.7	Menkent	148 21.9	S36 21.5
22	276 36.1	117 51.0	29.2	78 04.0	14.0	315 22.2	10.8	256 50.9	35.7	Miaplacidus	221 43.0	S69 42.6
23	291 38.6	132 50.7	28.0	93 05.1	14.6	330 25.0	10.9	271 53.4	35.7			
29 00	306 41.0	147 50.3	N10 26.8	108 06.2	S 8 15.2	345 27.8	S16 11.0	286 55.8	N 5 35.7	Mirfak	308 57.8	N49 50.8
01	321 43.5	162 50.0	25.7	123 07.4	15.7	0 30.5	11.1	301 58.3	35.7	Nunki	76 13.0	S26 17.8
02	336 46.0	177 49.6	24.5	138 08.5	16.3	15 33.3	11.2	317 00.7	35.7	Peacock	53 37.7	S56 44.4
03	351 48.4	192 49.3	23.3	153 09.6	16.9	30 36.1	11.3	332 03.2 ..	35.7	Pollux	243 42.9	N28 01.8
04	6 50.9	207 48.9	22.2	168 10.8	17.5	45 38.8	11.4	347 05.6	35.7	Procyon	245 12.7	N 5 13.8
05	21 53.4	222 48.6	21.0	183 11.9	18.0	60 41.6	11.5	2 08.1	35.7			
06	36 55.8	237 48.2	N10 19.8	198 13.0	S 8 18.6	75 44.4	S16 11.6	17 10.5	N 5 35.7	Rasalhague	96 17.4	N12 34.0
07	51 58.3	252 47.9	18.7	213 14.2	19.2	90 47.1	11.7	32 12.9	35.7	Regulus	207 56.7	N11 58.8
T 08	67 00.7	267 47.5	17.5	228 15.3	19.8	105 49.9	11.8	47 15.4	35.7	Rigel	281 23.9	S 8 12.3
U 09	82 03.2	282 47.2 ..	16.3	243 16.4 ..	20.4	120 52.7 ..	11.9	62 17.8 ..	35.7	Rigil Kent.	140 08.2	S60 49.6
E 10	97 05.7	297 46.8	15.1	258 17.6	20.9	135 55.5	12.0	77 20.3	35.7	Sabik	102 26.2	S15 43.2
S 11	112 08.1	312 46.5	14.0	273 18.7	21.5	150 58.2	12.1	92 22.7	35.7			
D 12	127 10.6	327 46.1	N10 12.8	288 19.8	S 8 22.1	166 01.0	S16 12.2	107 25.2	N 5 35.7	Schedar	349 54.0	N56 31.2
A 13	142 13.1	342 45.8	11.6	303 21.0	22.7	181 03.8	12.3	122 27.6	35.7	Shaula	96 38.0	S37 06.0
Y 14	157 15.5	357 45.4	10.5	318 22.1	23.2	196 06.5	12.4	137 30.1	35.7	Sirius	258 44.7	S16 42.8
15	172 18.0	12 45.1 ..	09.3	333 23.2 ..	23.8	211 09.3 ..	12.5	152 32.5 ..	35.7	Spica	158 44.1	S11 08.8
16	187 20.5	27 44.7	08.1	348 24.4	24.4	226 12.1	12.6	167 35.0	35.7	Suhail	223 01.7	S43 25.5
17	202 22.9	42 44.4	06.9	3 25.5	25.0	241 14.8	12.7	182 37.4	35.6			
18	217 25.4	57 44.1	N10 05.8	18 26.6	S 8 25.5	256 17.6	S16 12.8	197 39.9	N 5 35.6	Vega	80 46.8	N38 47.2
19	232 27.9	72 43.7	04.6	33 27.8	26.1	271 20.4	12.9	212 42.3	35.6	Zuben'ubi	137 18.8	S16 01.8
20	247 30.3	87 43.4	03.4	48 28.9	26.7	286 23.2	13.0	227 44.8	35.6			
21	262 32.8	102 43.0 ..	02.2	63 30.0 ..	27.3	301 25.9 ..	13.1	242 47.2 ..	35.6		SHA	Mer. Pass.
22	277 35.2	117 42.7	10 01.0	78 31.1	27.9	316 28.7	13.2	257 49.7	35.6	Venus	202 17.0	14 08
23	292 37.7	132 42.3	N 9 59.9	93 32.3	28.4	331 31.5	13.4	272 52.1	35.6	Mars	161 57.0	16 48
	h m									Jupiter	38 39.4	1 02
Mer. Pass.	3 36.6	v −0.4	d 1.2	v 1.1	d 0.6	v 2.8	d 0.1	v 2.4	d 0.0	Saturn	340 15.3	4 55

These pages (reduced) are produced from *The Nautical Almanac*.

Appendix A

1997 JULY 27, 28, 29 (SUN., MON., TUES.)

UT	SUN GHA	SUN Dec	MOON GHA	v	MOON Dec	d	HP
d h	° '	° '	° '	'	° '	'	'
27 00	178 22.9	N19 15.1	268 51.5	9.9	N10 18.8	9.0	58.3
01	193 22.9	14.5	283 20.4	9.9	10 27.8	9.0	58.3
02	208 22.9	13.9	297 49.3	9.9	10 36.8	8.8	58.3
03	223 22.9	.. 13.4	312 18.2	9.8	10 45.6	8.8	58.2
04	238 22.9	12.8	326 47.0	9.9	10 54.4	8.7	58.2
05	253 22.9	12.2	341 15.9	9.9	11 03.1	8.7	58.2
06	268 22.9	N19 11.7	355 44.8	9.8	N11 11.8	8.6	58.2
07	283 23.0	11.1	10 13.6	9.9	11 20.4	8.5	58.1
S 08	298 23.0	10.5	24 42.5	9.9	11 28.9	8.4	58.1
U 09	313 23.0	.. 10.0	39 11.4	9.8	11 37.3	8.4	58.1
N 10	328 23.0	09.4	53 40.2	9.9	11 45.7	8.3	58.0
11	343 23.0	08.8	68 09.1	9.8	11 54.0	8.2	58.0
D 12	358 23.0	N19 08.3	82 37.9	9.9	N12 02.2	8.1	58.0
A 13	13 23.0	07.7	97 06.8	9.8	12 10.3	8.1	58.0
Y 14	28 23.0	07.1	111 35.6	9.9	12 18.4	8.0	57.9
15	43 23.0	.. 06.6	126 04.5	9.8	12 26.4	7.9	57.9
16	58 23.0	06.0	140 33.3	9.9	12 34.3	7.8	57.9
17	73 23.0	05.4	155 02.2	9.8	12 42.1	7.8	57.8
18	88 23.0	N19 04.8	169 31.0	9.9	N12 49.9	7.7	57.8
19	103 23.1	04.3	183 59.9	9.8	12 57.6	7.6	57.8
20	118 23.1	03.7	198 28.7	9.8	13 05.2	7.5	57.8
21	133 23.1	.. 03.1	212 57.5	9.9	13 12.7	7.4	57.7
22	148 23.1	02.5	227 26.4	9.8	13 20.1	7.4	57.7
23	163 23.1	02.0	241 55.2	9.8	13 27.5	7.3	57.7
28 00	178 23.1	N19 01.4	256 24.0	9.8	N13 34.8	7.2	57.7
01	193 23.1	00.8	270 52.8	9.8	13 42.0	7.1	57.6
02	208 23.1	19 00.2	285 21.6	9.9	13 49.1	7.0	57.6
03	223 23.1	18 59.7	299 50.5	9.8	13 56.1	6.9	57.6
04	238 23.2	59.1	314 19.3	9.8	14 03.0	6.9	57.5
05	253 23.2	58.5	328 48.1	9.8	14 09.9	6.8	57.5
06	268 23.2	N18 57.9	343 16.9	9.8	N14 16.7	6.7	57.5
07	283 23.2	57.3	357 45.7	9.8	14 23.4	6.6	57.5
M 08	298 23.2	56.8	12 14.5	9.7	14 30.0	6.5	57.4
O 09	313 23.2	.. 56.2	26 43.2	9.8	14 36.5	6.5	57.4
N 10	328 23.2	55.6	41 12.0	9.8	14 43.0	6.3	57.4
11	343 23.2	55.0	55 40.8	9.8	14 49.3	6.3	57.4
D 12	358 23.3	N18 54.4	70 09.6	9.8	N14 55.6	6.2	57.3
A 13	13 23.3	53.9	84 38.4	9.7	15 01.8	6.1	57.3
Y 14	28 23.3	53.3	99 07.1	9.8	15 07.9	6.0	57.3
15	43 23.3	.. 52.7	113 35.9	9.8	15 13.9	5.9	57.3
16	58 23.3	52.1	128 04.7	9.8	15 19.8	5.8	57.2
17	73 23.3	51.5	142 33.5	9.7	15 25.6	5.7	57.2
18	88 23.3	N18 50.9	157 02.2	9.8	N15 31.3	5.7	57.2
19	103 23.4	50.3	171 31.0	9.7	15 37.0	5.5	57.1
20	118 23.4	49.8	185 59.7	9.8	15 42.5	5.5	57.1
21	133 23.4	.. 49.2	200 28.5	9.8	15 48.0	5.4	57.1
22	148 23.4	48.6	214 57.3	9.7	15 53.4	5.3	57.1
23	163 23.4	48.0	229 26.0	9.8	15 58.7	5.1	57.0
29 00	178 23.4	N18 47.4	243 54.8	9.7	N16 03.8	5.1	57.0
01	193 23.5	46.8	258 23.5	9.8	16 08.9	5.0	57.0
02	208 23.5	46.2	272 52.3	9.7	16 13.9	5.0	57.0
03	223 23.5	.. 45.6	287 21.0	9.8	16 18.9	4.8	56.9
04	238 23.5	45.0	301 49.8	9.8	16 23.7	4.7	56.9
05	253 23.5	44.5	316 18.6	9.7	16 28.4	4.6	56.9
06	268 23.6	N18 43.9	330 47.3	9.8	N16 33.0	4.6	56.9
07	283 23.6	43.3	345 16.1	9.7	16 37.6	4.4	56.8
T 08	298 23.6	42.7	359 44.8	9.8	16 42.0	4.4	56.8
U 09	313 23.6	.. 42.1	14 13.6	9.7	16 46.4	4.2	56.8
E 10	328 23.6	41.5	28 42.3	9.8	16 50.6	4.2	56.8
S 11	343 23.7	40.9	43 11.1	9.8	16 54.8	4.1	56.7
D 12	358 23.7	N18 40.3	57 39.9	9.7	N16 58.9	3.9	56.7
A 13	13 23.7	39.7	72 08.6	9.8	17 02.8	3.9	56.7
Y 14	28 23.7	39.1	86 37.4	9.8	17 06.7	3.8	56.7
15	43 23.7	.. 38.5	101 06.2	9.8	17 10.5	3.7	56.6
16	58 23.8	37.9	115 35.0	9.7	17 14.2	3.6	56.6
17	73 23.8	37.3	130 03.7	9.8	17 17.8	3.4	56.6
18	88 23.8	N18 36.7	144 32.5	9.8	N17 21.2	3.4	56.6
19	103 23.8	36.1	159 01.3	9.8	17 24.6	3.3	56.5
20	118 23.8	35.5	173 30.1	9.8	17 27.9	3.2	56.5
21	133 23.9	.. 34.9	187 58.9	9.8	17 31.1	3.1	56.5
22	148 23.9	34.3	202 27.7	9.9	17 34.2	3.1	56.5
23	163 23.9	33.7	216 56.6	9.8	N17 37.3	2.9	56.4
	SD 15.8	d 0.6	SD 15.8		15.6		15.5

Twilight, Sunrise and Moonrise

Lat.	Naut.	Civil	Sunrise	Moonrise 27	28	29	30
°	h m	h m	h m	h m	h m	h m	h m
N 72	□	□	□	21 45	21 39	21 29	□
N 70	////	////	00 36	22 10	22 17	22 32	23 03
68	////	////	01 53	22 29	22 44	23 07	23 45
66	////	////	02 30	22 44	23 04	23 33	24 14
64	////	01 13	02 55	22 56	23 20	23 52	24 35
62	////	01 58	03 15	23 07	23 34	24 09	00 09
60	////	02 27	03 31	23 16	23 46	24 22	00 22
N 58	01 06	02 49	03 45	23 24	23 56	24 34	00 34
56	01 48	03 06	03 56	23 31	24 04	00 04	00 44
54	02 14	03 21	04 07	23 37	24 12	00 12	00 53
52	02 35	03 33	04 16	23 43	24 19	00 19	01 01
50	02 51	03 44	04 24	23 48	24 26	00 26	01 08
45	03 23	04 06	04 41	23 59	24 39	00 39	01 23
N 40	03 46	04 24	04 55	24 09	00 09	00 51	01 36
35	04 04	04 38	05 06	24 17	00 17	01 00	01 47
30	04 19	04 50	05 17	24 24	00 24	01 09	01 56
20	04 42	05 10	05 34	24 36	00 36	01 24	02 13
N 10	05 00	05 27	05 49	24 47	00 47	01 36	02 27
0	05 16	05 41	06 03	00 05	00 57	01 49	02 40
S 10	05 29	05 55	06 17	00 13	01 07	02 01	02 54
20	05 41	06 08	06 31	00 21	01 18	02 14	03 08
30	05 54	06 23	06 48	00 31	01 31	02 29	03 25
35	06 00	06 31	06 58	00 36	01 38	02 38	03 34
40	06 07	06 40	07 09	00 42	01 46	02 48	03 45
45	06 14	06 50	07 22	00 50	01 56	02 59	03 58
S 50	06 22	07 01	07 37	00 58	02 08	03 14	04 14
52	06 25	07 07	07 44	01 02	02 13	03 20	04 22
54	06 29	07 13	07 52	01 07	02 20	03 28	04 30
56	06 33	07 19	08 02	01 12	02 26	03 36	04 39
58	06 37	07 26	08 12	01 17	02 34	03 45	04 50
S 60	06 42	07 34	08 24	01 24	02 43	03 56	05 02

Sunset, Twilight and Moonset

Lat.	Sunset	Civil	Naut.	Moonset 27	28	29	30
°	h m	h m	h m	h m	h m	h m	h m
N 72	□	□	□	15 26	17 21	19 19	□
N 70	23 21	////	////	15 03	16 44	18 17	19 33
68	22 15	////	////	14 45	16 18	17 41	18 51
66	21 40	////	////	14 31	15 58	17 16	18 22
64	21 15	22 54	////	14 20	15 42	16 57	18 00
62	20 56	22 11	////	14 10	15 29	16 41	17 43
60	20 40	21 43	////	14 01	15 18	16 28	17 29
N 58	20 27	21 22	23 01	13 54	15 08	16 16	17 16
56	20 15	21 05	22 22	13 47	15 00	16 06	17 06
54	20 05	20 51	21 56	13 42	14 52	15 58	16 56
52	19 56	20 38	21 36	13 36	14 46	15 50	16 48
50	19 48	20 28	21 20	13 32	14 40	15 43	16 41
45	19 32	20 06	20 49	13 22	14 27	15 28	16 25
N 40	19 18	19 48	20 26	13 13	14 16	15 16	16 11
35	19 06	19 34	20 08	13 06	14 07	15 05	16 00
30	18 56	19 22	19 54	12 59	13 59	14 56	15 50
20	18 39	19 02	19 30	12 49	13 45	14 40	15 34
N 10	18 24	18 46	19 12	12 39	13 33	14 26	15 19
0	18 10	18 32	18 57	12 30	13 22	14 13	15 05
S 10	17 56	18 18	18 44	12 21	13 10	14 01	14 51
20	17 42	18 05	18 32	12 11	12 58	13 47	14 37
30	17 25	17 50	18 19	12 01	12 45	13 31	14 20
35	17 16	17 43	18 13	11 54	12 37	13 22	14 10
40	17 05	17 34	18 07	11 47	12 28	13 11	13 59
45	16 52	17 24	17 59	11 39	12 17	12 59	13 45
S 50	16 36	17 12	17 52	11 29	12 05	12 44	13 29
52	16 29	17 07	17 48	11 24	11 59	12 37	13 22
54	16 21	17 01	17 44	11 19	11 52	12 30	13 13
56	16 12	16 54	17 40	11 14	11 45	12 21	13 04
58	16 02	16 47	17 36	11 08	11 37	12 12	12 53
S 60	15 50	16 39	17 31	11 01	11 28	12 00	12 41

Day	SUN Eqn. of Time 00h	12h	Mer. Pass.	MOON Mer. Pass. Upper	Lower	Age	Phase
d	m s	m s	h m	h m	h m	d	%
27	06 28	06 28	12 06	06 18	18 43	23	42
28	06 28	06 27	12 06	07 09	19 35	24	32
29	06 26	06 25	12 06	08 01	20 27	25	22

Appendix B

UT	ARIES GHA	VENUS −4.7 GHA	Dec	MARS +1.2 GHA	Dec	JUPITER −2.2 GHA	Dec	SATURN +0.6 GHA	Dec	STARS Name	SHA	Dec
6 00	74 49.0	135 51.1	S23 21.2	142 29.9	S23 07.0	114 44.2	S16 28.8	61 15.1	N 2 57.6	Acamar	315 27.0	S40 19.0
01	89 51.5	150 51.9	20.6	157 30.3	06.7	129 46.2	28.7	76 17.6	57.6	Achernar	335 35.3	S57 15.1
02	104 54.0	165 52.7	20.1	172 30.7	06.4	144 48.3	28.6	91 20.1	57.6	Acrux	173 22.8	S63 04.9
03	119 56.4	180 53.5	.. 19.5	187 31.1	.. 06.1	159 50.4	.. 28.4	106 22.6	.. 57.6	Adhara	255 21.5	S28 58.2
04	134 58.9	195 54.3	19.0	202 31.5	05.8	174 52.4	28.3	121 25.1	57.6	Aldebaran	291 02.7	N16 30.2
05	150 01.3	210 55.1	18.4	217 31.9	05.5	189 54.5	28.2	136 27.6	57.5			
06	165 03.8	225 55.9	S23 17.9	232 32.2	S23 05.2	204 56.5	S16 28.1	151 30.1	N 2 57.5	Alioth	166 31.5	N55 58.1
07	180 06.3	240 56.7	17.3	247 32.6	04.9	219 58.6	27.9	166 32.7	57.5	Alkaid	153 08.7	N49 19.3
S 08	195 08.7	255 57.5	16.8	262 33.0	04.6	235 00.6	27.8	181 35.2	57.5	Al Na'ir	27 58.8	S46 58.4
A 09	210 11.2	270 58.3	.. 16.2	277 33.4	.. 04.3	250 02.7	.. 27.7	196 37.7	.. 57.5	Alnilam	275 58.1	S 1 12.3
T 10	225 13.7	285 59.2	15.7	292 33.8	04.0	265 04.7	27.5	211 40.2	57.5	Alphard	218 07.6	S 8 39.0
U 11	240 16.1	301 00.0	15.1	307 34.2	03.7	280 06.8	27.4	226 42.7	57.5			
R 12	255 18.6	316 00.8	S23 14.5	322 34.5	S23 03.4	295 08.8	S16 27.3	241 45.2	N 2 57.5	Alphecca	126 21.5	N26 43.4
D 13	270 21.1	331 01.6	14.0	337 34.9	03.1	310 10.9	27.1	256 47.7	57.5	Alpheratz	357 55.7	N29 04.9
A 14	285 23.5	346 02.4	13.4	352 35.3	02.8	325 12.9	27.0	271 50.2	57.5	Altair	62 20.1	N 8 52.0
Y 15	300 26.0	1 03.3	.. 12.9	7 35.7	.. 02.5	340 15.0	.. 26.9	286 52.7	.. 57.5	Ankaa	353 27.3	S42 19.3
16	315 28.5	16 04.1	12.3	22 36.1	02.2	355 17.0	26.8	301 55.2	57.5	Antares	112 41.2	S26 25.4
17	330 30.9	31 04.9	11.8	37 36.5	01.9	10 19.1	26.6	316 57.7	57.5			
18	345 33.4	46 05.8	S23 11.2	52 36.9	S23 01.6	25 21.1	S16 26.5	332 00.3	N 2 57.4	Arcturus	146 06.9	N19 11.7
19	0 35.8	61 06.6	10.7	67 37.2	01.3	40 23.2	26.4	347 02.8	57.4	Atria	107 54.3	S69 01.3
20	15 38.3	76 07.5	10.1	82 37.6	01.0	55 25.2	26.2	2 05.3	57.4	Avior	234 22.4	S59 30.0
21	30 40.8	91 08.3	.. 09.5	97 38.0	.. 00.7	70 27.3	.. 26.1	17 07.8	.. 57.4	Bellatrix	278 44.4	N 6 20.7
22	45 43.2	106 09.1	09.0	112 38.4	00.4	85 29.3	26.0	32 10.3	57.4	Betelgeuse	271 13.8	N 7 24.3
23	60 45.7	121 10.0	08.4	127 38.8	23 00.1	100 31.4	25.8	47 12.8	57.4			
7 00	75 48.2	136 10.8	S23 07.9	142 39.2	S22 59.8	115 33.4	S16 25.7	62 15.3	N 2 57.4	Canopus	264 00.9	S52 41.7
01	90 50.6	151 11.7	07.3	157 39.5	59.5	130 35.5	25.6	77 17.8	57.4	Capella	280 51.5	N45 59.6
02	105 53.1	166 12.6	06.7	172 39.9	59.1	145 37.5	25.5	92 20.3	57.4	Deneb	49 39.8	N45 16.7
03	120 55.6	181 13.4	.. 06.2	187 40.3	.. 58.8	160 39.6	.. 25.3	107 22.8	.. 57.4	Denebola	182 45.9	N14 35.0
04	135 58.0	196 14.3	05.6	202 40.7	58.5	175 41.6	25.2	122 25.3	57.4	Diphda	349 07.7	S18 00.0
05	151 00.5	211 15.1	05.1	217 41.1	58.2	190 43.7	25.1	137 27.8	57.4			
06	166 02.9	226 16.0	S23 04.5	232 41.5	S22 57.9	205 45.7	S16 24.9	152 30.3	N 2 57.4	Dubhe	194 06.3	N61 45.4
07	181 05.4	241 16.9	03.9	247 41.9	57.6	220 47.8	24.8	167 32.9	57.4	Elnath	278 27.3	N28 36.2
S 08	196 07.9	256 17.8	03.4	262 42.3	57.3	235 49.8	24.7	182 35.4	57.3	Eltanin	90 52.2	N51 29.6
U 09	211 10.3	271 18.6	.. 02.8	277 42.6	.. 57.0	250 51.9	.. 24.5	197 37.9	.. 57.3	Enif	33 58.9	N 9 52.1
N 10	226 12.8	286 19.5	02.2	292 43.0	56.7	265 53.9	24.4	212 40.4	57.3	Fomalhaut	15 37.1	S29 38.1
11	241 15.3	301 20.4	01.7	307 43.4	56.4	280 56.0	24.3	227 42.9	57.3			
D 12	256 17.7	316 21.3	S23 01.1	322 43.8	S22 56.0	295 58.0	S16 24.1	242 45.4	N 2 57.3	Gacrux	172 14.3	S57 05.8
A 13	271 20.2	331 22.2	00.6	337 44.2	55.7	311 00.1	24.0	257 47.9	57.3	Gienah	176 04.6	S17 31.7
Y 14	286 22.7	346 23.1	23 00.0	352 44.6	55.4	326 02.1	23.9	272 50.4	57.3	Hadar	149 05.2	S60 21.4
15	301 25.1	1 24.0	22 59.4	7 45.0	.. 55.1	341 04.2	.. 23.8	287 52.9	.. 57.3	Hamal	328 13.9	N23 27.2
16	316 27.6	16 24.9	58.9	22 45.3	54.8	356 06.2	23.6	302 55.4	57.3	Kaus Aust.	84 00.0	S34 23.0
17	331 30.1	31 25.8	58.3	37 45.7	54.5	11 08.3	23.5	317 57.9	57.3			
18	346 32.5	46 26.7	S22 57.7	52 46.1	S22 54.2	26 10.3	S16 23.4	333 00.4	N 2 57.3	Kochab	137 20.8	N74 09.8
19	1 35.0	61 27.6	57.2	67 46.5	53.8	41 12.3	23.2	348 02.9	57.3	Markab	13 50.2	N15 11.8
20	16 37.4	76 28.5	56.6	82 46.9	53.5	56 14.4	23.1	3 05.4	57.3	Menkar	314 27.2	N 4 04.8
21	31 39.9	91 29.4	.. 56.0	97 47.3	.. 53.2	71 16.4	.. 23.0	18 07.9	.. 57.3	Menkent	148 21.9	S36 21.3
22	46 42.4	106 30.3	55.5	112 47.7	52.9	86 18.5	22.8	33 10.4	57.3	Miaplacidus	221 41.6	S69 42.3
23	61 44.8	121 31.2	54.9	127 48.1	52.6	101 20.5	22.7	48 12.9	57.3			
8 00	76 47.3	136 32.1	S22 54.3	142 48.4	S22 52.3	116 22.6	S16 22.6	63 15.4	N 2 57.3	Mirfak	308 56.9	N49 51.2
01	91 49.8	151 33.1	53.8	157 48.8	51.9	131 24.6	22.4	78 17.9	57.3	Nunki	76 13.4	S26 17.9
02	106 52.2	166 34.0	53.2	172 49.2	51.6	146 26.7	22.3	93 20.4	57.3	Peacock	53 38.4	S56 44.6
03	121 54.7	181 34.9	.. 52.6	187 49.6	.. 51.3	161 28.7	.. 22.2	108 23.0	.. 57.2	Pollux	243 42.0	N28 01.7
04	136 57.2	196 35.8	52.1	202 50.0	51.0	176 30.7	22.0	123 25.5	57.2	Procyon	245 11.9	N 5 13.7
05	151 59.6	211 36.8	51.5	217 50.4	50.7	191 32.8	21.9	138 28.0	57.2			
06	167 02.1	226 37.7	S22 50.9	232 50.8	S22 50.0	206 34.8	S16 21.8	153 30.5	N 2 57.2	Rasalhague	96 17.8	N12 33.9
07	182 04.5	241 38.6	50.4	247 51.2	50.0	221 36.9	21.6	168 33.0	57.2	Regulus	207 56.1	N11 58.6
08	197 07.0	256 39.6	49.8	262 51.5	49.7	236 38.9	21.5	183 35.5	57.2	Rigel	281 23.2	S 8 12.4
M 09	212 09.5	271 40.5	.. 49.2	277 51.9	.. 49.4	251 41.0	.. 21.4	198 38.0	.. 57.2	Rigil Kent.	140 08.5	S60 49.2
O 10	227 11.9	286 41.5	48.6	292 52.3	49.1	266 43.0	21.2	213 40.5	57.2	Sabik	102 26.5	S15 43.2
N 11	242 14.4	301 42.4	48.1	307 52.7	48.7	281 45.1	21.1	228 43.0	57.2			
D 12	257 16.9	316 43.4	S22 47.5	322 53.1	S22 48.4	296 47.1	S16 21.0	243 45.5	N 2 57.2	Schedar	349 53.8	N56 31.8
A 13	272 19.3	331 44.3	46.9	337 53.5	48.1	311 49.1	20.8	258 48.0	57.2	Shaula	96 38.5	S37 06.0
Y 14	287 21.8	346 45.3	46.4	352 53.9	47.8	326 51.2	20.7	273 50.5	57.2	Sirius	258 43.9	S16 42.8
15	302 24.3	1 46.3	.. 45.8	7 54.3	.. 47.4	341 53.2	.. 20.6	288 53.0	.. 57.2	Spica	158 44.0	S11 08.9
16	317 26.7	16 47.2	45.2	22 54.7	47.1	356 55.3	20.4	303 55.5	57.2	Suhail	223 00.9	S43 25.3
17	332 29.2	31 48.2	44.6	37 55.0	46.8	11 57.3	20.3	318 58.0	57.2			
18	347 31.7	46 49.2	S22 44.1	52 55.4	S22 46.5	26 59.3	S16 20.2	334 00.5	N 2 57.2	Vega	80 47.4	N38 47.2
19	2 34.1	61 50.1	43.5	67 55.8	46.1	42 01.4	20.0	349 03.0	57.2	Zuben'ubi	137 18.9	S16 01.8
20	17 36.6	76 51.1	42.9	82 56.2	45.8	57 03.4	19.9	4 05.5	57.2		SHA	Mer. Pass.
21	32 39.0	91 52.1	.. 42.4	97 56.6	.. 45.5	72 05.5	.. 19.8	19 08.0	.. 57.2		o '	h m
22	47 41.5	106 53.1	41.8	112 57.0	45.2	87 07.5	19.6	34 10.5	57.2	Venus	60 22.7	14 54
23	62 44.0	121 54.0	41.2	127 57.4	44.8	102 09.6	19.5	49 13.0	57.2	Mars	66 51.0	14 29
	h m									Jupiter	39 45.3	16 16
Mer. Pass.	18 53.7	v 0.9	d 0.6	v 0.4	d 0.3	v 2.0	d 0.1	v 2.5	d 0.0	Saturn	346 27.1	19 48

Appendix B

1997 DECEMBER 6, 7, 8 (SAT., SUN., MON.)   237

SUN / MOON

UT	SUN GHA	Dec	MOON GHA	v	Dec	d	HP
d h	° ′	° ′	° ′	′	° ′	′	′
6 00	182 16.9	S22 28.0	105 32.9	9.2	S10 52.5	9.2	58.8
01	197 16.6	28.3	120 01.1	9.2	10 43.3	9.2	58.8
02	212 16.4	28.6	134 29.3	9.3	10 34.1	9.4	58.8
03	227 16.1	.. 28.9	148 57.6	9.3	10 24.7	9.3	58.9
04	242 15.8	29.2	163 25.9	9.2	10 15.4	9.5	58.9
05	257 15.6	29.5	177 54.1	9.3	10 05.9	9.4	58.9
06	272 15.3	S22 29.8	192 22.4	9.4	S 9 56.5	9.6	58.9
S 07	287 15.0	30.1	206 50.8	9.3	9 46.9	9.6	58.9
A 08	302 14.8	30.4	221 19.1	9.4	9 37.3	9.7	58.9
T 09	317 14.5	.. 30.7	235 47.5	9.4	9 27.6	9.7	58.9
U 10	332 14.3	31.0	250 15.9	9.4	9 17.9	9.8	58.9
R 11	347 14.0	31.2	264 44.3	9.4	9 08.1	9.9	58.9
D 12	2 13.7	S22 31.5	279 12.7	9.4	S 8 58.2	9.9	59.0
A 13	17 13.5	31.8	293 41.1	9.5	8 48.3	9.9	59.0
Y 14	32 13.2	32.1	308 09.6	9.5	8 38.4	10.0	59.0
15	47 12.9	.. 32.4	322 38.1	9.5	8 28.4	10.1	59.0
16	62 12.7	32.7	337 06.6	9.5	8 18.3	10.1	59.0
17	77 12.4	33.0	351 35.1	9.5	8 08.2	10.2	59.0
18	92 12.1	S22 33.3	6 03.6	9.6	S 7 58.0	10.2	59.0
19	107 11.9	33.6	20 32.2	9.5	7 47.8	10.2	59.0
20	122 11.6	33.9	35 00.7	9.6	7 37.6	10.3	59.0
21	137 11.3	.. 34.2	49 29.3	9.6	7 27.3	10.4	59.1
22	152 11.1	34.4	63 57.9	9.6	7 16.9	10.4	59.1
23	167 10.8	34.7	78 26.5	9.6	7 06.5	10.4	59.1
7 00	182 10.5	S22 35.0	92 55.1	9.7	S 6 56.1	10.5	59.1
01	197 10.3	35.3	107 23.8	9.6	6 45.6	10.6	59.1
02	212 10.0	35.6	121 52.4	9.7	6 35.0	10.5	59.1
03	227 09.7	.. 35.9	136 21.1	9.7	6 24.5	10.6	59.1
04	242 09.4	36.1	150 49.8	9.7	6 13.9	10.7	59.1
05	257 09.2	36.4	165 18.5	9.7	6 03.2	10.7	59.1
06	272 08.9	S22 36.7	179 47.2	9.7	S 5 52.5	10.7	59.1
S 07	287 08.6	37.0	194 15.9	9.7	5 41.8	10.8	59.2
U 08	302 08.4	37.3	208 44.6	9.7	5 31.0	10.8	59.2
N 09	317 08.1	.. 37.5	223 13.3	9.8	5 20.2	10.8	59.2
10	332 07.8	37.8	237 42.1	9.7	5 09.4	10.9	59.2
11	347 07.6	38.1	252 10.8	9.8	4 58.5	10.9	59.2
D 12	2 07.3	S22 38.4	266 39.6	9.8	S 4 47.6	10.9	59.2
A 13	17 07.0	38.6	281 08.4	9.7	4 36.7	10.9	59.2
Y 14	32 06.8	38.9	295 37.1	9.8	4 25.8	11.0	59.2
15	47 06.5	.. 39.2	310 05.9	9.8	4 14.8	11.0	59.2
16	62 06.2	39.5	324 34.7	9.8	4 03.8	11.1	59.2
17	77 05.9	39.7	339 03.5	9.8	3 52.7	11.0	59.2
18	92 05.7	S22 40.0	353 32.3	9.8	S 3 41.7	11.1	59.2
19	107 05.4	40.3	8 01.1	9.8	3 30.6	11.1	59.3
20	122 05.1	40.6	22 29.9	9.8	3 19.5	11.2	59.3
21	137 04.9	.. 40.8	36 58.7	9.8	3 08.3	11.1	59.3
22	152 04.6	41.1	51 27.5	9.8	2 57.2	11.2	59.3
23	167 04.3	41.4	65 56.3	9.9	2 46.0	11.2	59.3
8 00	182 04.0	S22 41.6	80 25.2	9.8	S 2 34.8	11.2	59.3
01	197 03.8	41.9	94 54.0	9.8	2 23.6	11.2	59.3
02	212 03.5	42.2	109 22.8	9.8	2 12.4	11.3	59.3
03	227 03.2	.. 42.4	123 51.6	9.8	2 01.1	11.2	59.3
04	242 02.9	42.7	138 20.4	9.8	1 49.9	11.3	59.3
05	257 02.7	42.9	152 49.2	9.9	1 38.6	11.3	59.3
06	272 02.4	S22 43.2	167 18.1	9.8	S 1 27.3	11.3	59.3
07	287 02.1	43.5	181 46.9	9.8	1 16.0	11.3	59.3
08	302 01.8	43.7	196 15.7	9.8	1 04.7	11.3	59.3
M 09	317 01.6	.. 44.0	210 44.5	9.8	0 53.4	11.3	59.3
O 10	332 01.3	44.2	225 13.3	9.8	0 42.1	11.4	59.4
N 11	347 01.0	44.5	239 42.1	9.8	0 30.7	11.3	59.4
D 12	2 00.7	S22 44.8	254 10.9	9.8	S 0 19.4	11.4	59.4
A 13	17 00.5	45.0	268 39.7	9.7	S 0 08.0	11.3	59.4
Y 14	32 00.2	45.3	283 08.4	9.8	N 0 03.3	11.3	59.4
15	46 59.9	.. 45.5	297 37.2	9.8	0 14.6	11.4	59.4
16	61 59.6	45.8	312 06.0	9.7	0 26.0	11.3	59.4
17	76 59.4	46.0	326 34.7	9.8	0 37.3	11.4	59.4
18	91 59.1	S22 46.3	341 03.5	9.7	N 0 48.7	11.3	59.4
19	106 58.8	46.5	355 32.2	9.7	1 00.0	11.4	59.4
20	121 58.5	46.8	10 00.9	9.8	1 11.4	11.3	59.4
21	136 58.3	.. 47.0	24 29.7	9.7	1 22.7	11.3	59.4
22	151 58.0	47.3	38 58.4	9.7	1 34.0	11.3	59.4
23	166 57.7	47.5	53 27.1	9.6	N 1 45.3	11.4	59.4
	SD 16.3	d 0.3	SD 16.1	·	16.1		16.2

Twilight / Sunrise / Moonrise

Lat.	Twilight Naut.	Civil	Sunrise	Moonrise 6	7	8	9
°	h m	h m	h m	h m	h m	h m	h m
N 72	08 06	10 17	■	13 21	13 15	13 09	13 03
N 70	07 48	09 29	■	13 08	13 08	13 09	13 09
68	07 33	08 59	11 19	12 57	13 03	13 08	13 14
66	07 21	08 36	10 07	12 48	12 59	13 08	13 18
64	07 11	08 18	09 31	12 41	12 55	13 08	13 21
62	07 02	08 03	09 06	12 34	12 52	13 08	13 24
60	06 54	07 50	08 46	12 28	12 49	13 08	13 27
N 58	06 47	07 39	08 30	12 23	12 46	13 07	13 29
56	06 41	07 30	08 16	12 19	12 44	13 07	13 31
54	06 35	07 21	08 04	12 15	12 42	13 07	13 33
52	06 30	07 13	07 53	12 11	12 40	13 07	13 35
50	06 25	07 06	07 44	12 08	12 38	13 07	13 36
45	06 14	06 51	07 24	12 00	12 34	13 07	13 40
N 40	06 04	06 38	07 08	11 54	12 31	13 07	13 43
35	05 55	06 27	06 55	11 49	12 28	13 07	13 45
30	05 47	06 17	06 43	11 44	12 26	13 07	13 47
20	05 31	05 59	06 22	11 36	12 22	13 06	13 51
N 10	05 16	05 42	06 05	11 29	12 18	13 06	13 55
0	04 59	05 25	05 48	11 22	12 14	13 06	13 58
S 10	04 41	05 08	05 31	11 16	12 11	13 06	14 02
20	04 19	04 48	05 13	11 09	12 07	13 06	14 05
30	03 51	04 24	04 51	11 00	12 03	13 06	14 09
35	03 33	04 10	04 39	10 56	12 01	13 06	14 12
40	03 11	03 52	04 25	10 50	11 58	13 06	14 14
45	02 42	03 31	04 07	10 44	11 55	13 06	14 18
S 50	02 00	03 02	03 46	10 37	11 51	13 06	14 21
52	01 36	02 48	03 36	10 33	11 49	13 06	14 23
54	01 00	02 32	03 24	10 29	11 47	13 06	14 25
56	////	02 11	03 11	10 25	11 45	13 06	14 27
58	////	01 45	02 55	10 20	11 43	13 06	14 30
S 60	////	01 06	02 36	10 15	11 40	13 06	14 32

Sunset / Twilight / Moonset

Lat.	Sunset	Twilight Civil	Naut.	Moonset 6	7	8	9
°	h m	h m	h m	h m	h m	h m	h m
N 72	■	13 25	15 37	22 10	24 05	00 05	01 59
N 70	■	14 13	15 55	22 22	24 09	00 09	01 56
68	12 23	14 44	16 09	22 31	24 12	00 12	01 53
66	13 36	15 07	16 21	22 38	24 14	00 14	01 51
64	14 11	15 27	16 32	22 45	24 17	00 17	01 49
62	14 37	15 40	16 40	22 50	24 19	00 19	01 48
60	14 57	15 53	16 48	22 55	24 20	00 20	01 47
N 58	15 13	16 03	16 55	22 59	24 22	00 22	01 45
56	15 27	16 13	17 02	23 03	24 23	00 23	01 44
54	15 39	16 22	17 07	23 06	24 24	00 24	01 43
52	15 49	16 30	17 13	23 09	24 25	00 25	01 42
50	15 59	16 37	17 18	23 12	24 26	00 26	01 42
45	16 18	16 52	17 29	23 18	24 28	00 28	01 40
N 40	16 35	17 05	17 39	23 22	24 30	00 30	01 38
35	16 48	17 16	17 48	23 27	24 32	00 32	01 37
30	17 00	17 26	17 56	23 30	24 33	00 33	01 36
20	17 21	17 44	18 12	23 37	24 35	00 35	01 34
N 10	17 38	18 01	18 27	23 42	24 37	00 37	01 32
0	17 55	18 18	18 44	23 47	24 39	00 39	01 31
S 10	18 12	18 35	19 02	23 52	24 41	00 41	01 29
20	18 30	18 55	19 24	23 58	24 43	00 43	01 27
30	18 52	19 19	19 52	24 04	00 04	00 45	01 25
35	19 04	19 34	20 10	24 07	00 07	00 46	01 24
40	19 19	19 51	20 32	24 10	00 10	00 47	01 23
45	19 36	20 13	21 01	24 16	00 16	00 49	01 21
S 50	19 58	20 41	21 44	24 21	00 21	00 51	01 20
52	20 08	20 56	22 09	24 24	00 24	00 52	01 19
54	20 20	21 12	22 46	24 26	00 26	00 52	01 18
56	20 33	21 33	////	00 00	00 29	00 53	01 17
58	20 49	22 00	////	00 08	00 33	00 55	01 16
S 60	21 08	22 39	////	00 15	00 36	00 56	01 15

SUN / MOON

Day	SUN Eqn. of Time 00h	12h	Mer. Pass.	MOON Mer. Pass. Upper	Lower	Age	Phase
d	m s	m s	h m	h m	h m	d	%
6	09 08	08 55	11 51	17 35	05 09	06	42
7	08 43	08 30	11 52	18 27	06 01	07	53
8	08 17	08 04	11 52	19 18	06 53	08	64

56ᵐ — INCREMENTS AND CORRECTIONS — **57ᵐ**

56ᵐ

56ᵐ s	SUN PLANETS	ARIES	MOON	v or Corrⁿ d	v or Corrⁿ d	v or Corrⁿ d
00	14 00·0	14 02·3	13 21·7	0·0 0·0	6·0 5·7	12·0 11·3
01	14 00·3	14 02·6	13 22·0	0·1 0·1	6·1 5·7	12·1 11·4
02	14 00·5	14 02·8	13 22·2	0·2 0·2	6·2 5·8	12·2 11·5
03	14 00·8	14 03·1	13 22·4	0·3 0·3	6·3 5·9	12·3 11·6
04	14 01·0	14 03·3	13 22·7	0·4 0·4	6·4 6·0	12·4 11·7
05	14 01·3	14 03·6	13 22·9	0·5 0·5	6·5 6·1	12·5 11·8
06	14 01·5	14 03·8	13 23·2	0·6 0·6	6·6 6·2	12·6 11·9
07	14 01·8	14 04·1	13 23·4	0·7 0·7	6·7 6·3	12·7 12·0
08	14 02·0	14 04·3	13 23·6	0·8 0·8	6·8 6·4	12·8 12·1
09	14 02·3	14 04·6	13 23·9	0·9 0·8	6·9 6·5	12·9 12·1
10	14 02·5	14 04·8	13 24·1	1·0 0·9	7·0 6·6	13·0 12·2
11	14 02·8	14 05·1	13 24·4	1·1 1·0	7·1 6·7	13·1 12·3
12	14 03·0	14 05·3	13 24·6	1·2 1·1	7·2 6·8	13·2 12·4
13	14 03·3	14 05·6	13 24·8	1·3 1·2	7·3 6·9	13·3 12·5
14	14 03·5	14 05·8	13 25·1	1·4 1·3	7·4 7·0	13·4 12·6
15	14 03·8	14 06·1	13 25·3	1·5 1·4	7·5 7·1	13·5 12·7
16	14 04·0	14 06·3	13 25·6	1·6 1·5	7·6 7·2	13·6 12·8
17	14 04·3	14 06·6	13 25·8	1·7 1·6	7·7 7·3	13·7 12·9
18	14 04·5	14 06·8	13 26·0	1·8 1·7	7·8 7·3	13·8 13·0
19	14 04·8	14 07·1	13 26·3	1·9 1·8	7·9 7·4	13·9 13·1
20	14 05·0	14 07·3	13 26·5	2·0 1·9	8·0 7·5	14·0 13·2
21	14 05·3	14 07·6	13 26·7	2·1 2·0	8·1 7·6	14·1 13·3
22	14 05·5	14 07·8	13 27·0	2·2 2·1	8·2 7·7	14·2 13·4
23	14 05·8	14 08·1	13 27·2	2·3 2·2	8·3 7·8	14·3 13·5
24	14 06·0	14 08·3	13 27·5	2·4 2·3	8·4 7·9	14·4 13·6
25	14 06·3	14 08·6	13 27·7	2·5 2·4	8·5 8·0	14·5 13·7
26	14 06·5	14 08·8	13 27·9	2·6 2·4	8·6 8·1	14·6 13·7
27	14 06·8	14 09·1	13 28·2	2·7 2·5	8·7 8·2	14·7 13·8
28	14 07·0	14 09·3	13 28·4	2·8 2·6	8·8 8·3	14·8 13·9
29	14 07·3	14 09·6	13 28·7	2·9 2·7	8·9 8·4	14·9 14·0
30	14 07·5	14 09·8	13 28·9	3·0 2·8	9·0 8·5	15·0 14·1
31	14 07·8	14 10·1	13 29·1	3·1 2·9	9·1 8·6	15·1 14·2
32	14 08·0	14 10·3	13 29·4	3·2 3·0	9·2 8·7	15·2 14·3
33	14 08·3	14 10·6	13 29·6	3·3 3·1	9·3 8·8	15·3 14·4
34	14 08·5	14 10·8	13 29·8	3·4 3·2	9·4 8·9	15·4 14·5
35	14 08·8	14 11·1	13 30·1	3·5 3·3	9·5 8·9	15·5 14·6
36	14 09·0	14 11·3	13 30·3	3·6 3·4	9·6 9·0	15·6 14·7
37	14 09·3	14 11·6	13 30·6	3·7 3·5	9·7 9·1	15·7 14·8
38	14 09·5	14 11·8	13 30·8	3·8 3·6	9·8 9·2	15·8 14·9
39	14 09·8	14 12·1	13 31·0	3·9 3·7	9·9 9·3	15·9 15·0
40	14 10·0	14 12·3	13 31·3	4·0 3·8	10·0 9·4	16·0 15·1
41	14 10·3	14 12·6	13 31·5	4·1 3·9	10·1 9·5	16·1 15·2
42	14 10·5	14 12·8	13 31·8	4·2 4·0	10·2 9·6	16·2 15·3
43	14 10·8	14 13·1	13 32·0	4·3 4·0	10·3 9·7	16·3 15·3
44	14 11·0	14 13·3	13 32·2	4·4 4·1	10·4 9·8	16·4 15·4
45	14 11·3	14 13·6	13 32·5	4·5 4·2	10·5 9·9	16·5 15·5
46	14 11·5	14 13·8	13 32·7	4·6 4·3	10·6 10·0	16·6 15·6
47	14 11·8	14 14·1	13 32·9	4·7 4·4	10·7 10·1	16·7 15·7
48	14 12·0	14 14·3	13 33·2	4·8 4·5	10·8 10·2	16·8 15·8
49	14 12·3	14 14·6	13 33·4	4·9 4·6	10·9 10·3	16·9 15·9
50	14 12·5	14 14·8	13 33·7	5·0 4·7	11·0 10·4	17·0 16·0
51	14 12·8	14 15·1	13 33·9	5·1 4·8	11·1 10·5	17·1 16·1
52	14 13·0	14 15·3	13 34·1	5·2 4·9	11·2 10·5	17·2 16·2
53	14 13·3	14 15·6	13 34·4	5·3 5·0	11·3 10·6	17·3 16·3
54	14 13·5	14 15·8	13 34·6	5·4 5·1	11·4 10·7	17·4 16·4
55	14 13·8	14 16·1	13 34·9	5·5 5·2	11·5 10·8	17·5 16·5
56	14 14·0	14 16·3	13 35·1	5·6 5·3	11·6 10·9	17·6 16·6
57	14 14·3	14 16·6	13 35·3	5·7 5·4	11·7 11·0	17·7 16·7
58	14 14·5	14 16·8	13 35·6	5·8 5·5	11·8 11·1	17·8 16·8
59	14 14·8	14 17·1	13 35·8	5·9 5·6	11·9 11·2	17·9 16·9
60	14 15·0	14 17·3	13 36·1	6·0 5·7	12·0 11·3	18·0 17·0

57ᵐ

57ᵐ s	SUN PLANETS	ARIES	MOON	v or Corrⁿ d	v or Corrⁿ d	v or Corrⁿ d
00	14 15·0	14 17·3	13 36·1	0·0 0·0	6·0 5·8	12·0 11·5
01	14 15·3	14 17·6	13 36·3	0·1 0·1	6·1 5·8	12·1 11·6
02	14 15·5	14 17·8	13 36·5	0·2 0·2	6·2 5·9	12·2 11·7
03	14 15·8	14 18·1	13 36·8	0·3 0·3	6·3 6·0	12·3 11·8
04	14 16·0	14 18·3	13 37·0	0·4 0·4	6·4 6·1	12·4 11·9
05	14 16·3	14 18·6	13 37·2	0·5 0·5	6·5 6·2	12·5 12·0
06	14 16·5	14 18·8	13 37·5	0·6 0·6	6·6 6·3	12·6 12·1
07	14 16·8	14 19·1	13 37·7	0·7 0·7	6·7 6·4	12·7 12·2
08	14 17·0	14 19·3	13 38·0	0·8 0·8	6·8 6·5	12·8 12·3
09	14 17·3	14 19·6	13 38·2	0·9 0·9	6·9 6·6	12·9 12·4
10	14 17·5	14 19·8	13 38·4	1·0 1·0	7·0 6·7	13·0 12·5
11	14 17·8	14 20·1	13 38·7	1·1 1·1	7·1 6·8	13·1 12·6
12	14 18·0	14 20·3	13 38·9	1·2 1·2	7·2 6·9	13·2 12·7
13	14 18·3	14 20·6	13 39·2	1·3 1·2	7·3 7·0	13·3 12·7
14	14 18·5	14 20·9	13 39·4	1·4 1·3	7·4 7·1	13·4 12·8
15	14 18·8	14 21·1	13 39·6	1·5 1·4	7·5 7·2	13·5 12·9
16	14 19·0	14 21·4	13 39·9	1·6 1·5	7·6 7·3	13·6 13·0
17	14 19·3	14 21·6	13 40·1	1·7 1·6	7·7 7·4	13·7 13·1
18	14 19·5	14 21·9	13 40·3	1·8 1·7	7·8 7·5	13·8 13·2
19	14 19·8	14 22·1	13 40·6	1·9 1·8	7·9 7·6	13·9 13·3
20	14 20·0	14 22·4	13 40·8	2·0 1·9	8·0 7·7	14·0 13·4
21	14 20·3	14 22·6	13 41·1	2·1 2·0	8·1 7·8	14·1 13·5
22	14 20·5	14 22·9	13 41·3	2·2 2·1	8·2 7·9	14·2 13·6
23	14 20·8	14 23·1	13 41·5	2·3 2·2	8·3 8·0	14·3 13·7
24	14 21·0	14 23·4	13 41·8	2·4 2·3	8·4 8·1	14·4 13·8
25	14 21·3	14 23·6	13 42·0	2·5 2·4	8·5 8·1	14·5 13·9
26	14 21·5	14 23·9	13 42·3	2·6 2·5	8·6 8·2	14·6 14·0
27	14 21·8	14 24·1	13 42·5	2·7 2·6	8·7 8·3	14·7 14·1
28	14 22·0	14 24·4	13 42·7	2·8 2·7	8·8 8·4	14·8 14·2
29	14 22·3	14 24·6	13 43·0	2·9 2·8	8·9 8·5	14·9 14·3
30	14 22·5	14 24·9	13 43·2	3·0 2·9	9·0 8·6	15·0 14·4
31	14 22·8	14 25·1	13 43·4	3·1 3·0	9·1 8·7	15·1 14·5
32	14 23·0	14 25·4	13 43·7	3·2 3·1	9·2 8·8	15·2 14·6
33	14 23·3	14 25·6	13 43·9	3·3 3·2	9·3 8·9	15·3 14·7
34	14 23·5	14 25·9	13 44·2	3·4 3·3	9·4 9·0	15·4 14·8
35	14 23·8	14 26·1	13 44·4	3·5 3·4	9·5 9·1	15·5 14·9
36	14 24·0	14 26·4	13 44·6	3·6 3·5	9·6 9·2	15·6 15·0
37	14 24·3	14 26·6	13 44·9	3·7 3·5	9·7 9·3	15·7 15·0
38	14 24·5	14 26·9	13 45·1	3·8 3·6	9·8 9·4	15·8 15·1
39	14 24·8	14 27·1	13 45·4	3·9 3·7	9·9 9·5	15·9 15·2
40	14 25·0	14 27·4	13 45·6	4·0 3·8	10·0 9·6	16·0 15·3
41	14 25·3	14 27·6	13 45·8	4·1 3·9	10·1 9·7	16·1 15·4
42	14 25·5	14 27·9	13 46·1	4·2 4·0	10·2 9·8	16·2 15·5
43	14 25·8	14 28·1	13 46·3	4·3 4·1	10·3 9·9	16·3 15·6
44	14 26·0	14 28·4	13 46·5	4·4 4·2	10·4 10·0	16·4 15·7
45	14 26·3	14 28·6	13 46·8	4·5 4·3	10·5 10·1	16·5 15·8
46	14 26·5	14 28·9	13 47·0	4·6 4·4	10·6 10·2	16·6 15·9
47	14 26·8	14 29·1	13 47·3	4·7 4·5	10·7 10·3	16·7 16·0
48	14 27·0	14 29·4	13 47·5	4·8 4·6	10·8 10·4	16·8 16·1
49	14 27·3	14 29·6	13 47·7	4·9 4·7	10·9 10·4	16·9 16·2
50	14 27·5	14 29·9	13 48·0	5·0 4·8	11·0 10·5	17·0 16·3
51	14 27·8	14 30·1	13 48·2	5·1 4·9	11·1 10·6	17·1 16·4
52	14 28·0	14 30·4	13 48·5	5·2 5·0	11·2 10·7	17·2 16·5
53	14 28·3	14 30·6	13 48·7	5·3 5·1	11·3 10·8	17·3 16·6
54	14 28·5	14 30·9	13 48·9	5·4 5·2	11·4 10·9	17·4 16·7
55	14 28·8	14 31·1	13 49·2	5·5 5·3	11·5 11·0	17·5 16·8
56	14 29·0	14 31·4	13 49·4	5·6 5·4	11·6 11·1	17·6 16·9
57	14 29·3	14 31·6	13 49·7	5·7 5·5	11·7 11·2	17·7 17·0
58	14 29·5	14 31·9	13 49·9	5·8 5·6	11·8 11·3	17·8 17·1
59	14 29·8	14 32·1	13 50·1	5·9 5·7	11·9 11·4	17·9 17·2
60	14 30·0	14 32·4	13 50·4	6·0 5·8	12·0 11·5	18·0 17·3

These pages (reduced) are produced from *The Nautical Almanac.*

Appendix D

ALTITUDE CORRECTION TABLES 10°–90°—SUN, STARS, PLANETS

SUN

OCT.–MAR. App. Alt.	Lower Limb	Upper Limb	APR.–SEPT. App. Alt.	Lower Limb	Upper Limb
9 34	+10·8	−21·5	9 39	+10·6	−21·2
9 45	+10·9	−21·4	9 51	+10·7	−21·1
9 56	+11·0	−21·3	10 03	+10·8	−21·0
10 08	+11·1	−21·2	10 15	+10·9	−20·9
10 21	+11·2	−21·1	10 27	+11·0	−20·8
10 34	+11·3	−21·0	10 40	+11·1	−20·7
10 47	+11·4	−20·9	10 54	+11·2	−20·6
11 01	+11·5	−20·8	11 08	+11·3	−20·5
11 15	+11·6	−20·7	11 23	+11·4	−20·4
11 30	+11·7	−20·6	11 38	+11·5	−20·3
11 46	+11·8	−20·5	11 54	+11·6	−20·2
12 02	+11·9	−20·4	12 10	+11·7	−20·1
12 19	+12·0	−20·3	12 28	+11·8	−20·0
12 37	+12·1	−20·2	12 46	+11·9	−19·9
12 55	+12·2	−20·1	13 05	+12·0	−19·8
13 14	+12·3	−20·0	13 24	+12·1	−19·7
13 35	+12·4	−19·9	13 45	+12·2	−19·6
13 56	+12·5	−19·8	14 07	+12·3	−19·5
14 18	+12·6	−19·7	14 30	+12·4	−19·4
14 42	+12·7	−19·6	14 54	+12·5	−19·3
15 06	+12·8	−19·5	15 19	+12·6	−19·2
15 32	+12·9	−19·4	15 46	+12·7	−19·1
15 59	+13·0	−19·3	16 14	+12·8	−19·0
16 28	+13·1	−19·2	16 44	+12·9	−18·9
16 59	+13·2	−19·1	17 15	+13·0	−18·8
17 32	+13·3	−19·0	17 48	+13·1	−18·7
18 06	+13·4	−18·9	18 24	+13·2	−18·6
18 42	+13·5	−18·8	19 01	+13·3	−18·5
19 21	+13·6	−18·7	19 42	+13·4	−18·4
20 03	+13·7	−18·6	20 25	+13·5	−18·3
20 48	+13·8	−18·5	21 11	+13·6	−18·2
21 35	+13·9	−18·4	22 00	+13·7	−18·1
22 26	+14·0	−18·3	22 54	+13·8	−18·0
23 22	+14·1	−18·2	23 51	+13·9	−17·9
24 21	+14·2	−18·1	24 53	+14·0	−17·8
25 26	+14·3	−18·0	26 00	+14·1	−17·7
26 36	+14·4	−17·9	27 13	+14·2	−17·6
27 52	+14·5	−17·8	28 33	+14·3	−17·5
29 15	+14·6	−17·7	30 00	+14·4	−17·4
30 46	+14·7	−17·6	31 35	+14·5	−17·3
32 26	+14·8	−17·5	33 20	+14·6	−17·2
34 17	+14·9	−17·4	35 17	+14·7	−17·1
36 20	+15·0	−17·3	37 26	+14·8	−17·0
38 36	+15·1	−17·2	39 50	+14·9	−16·9
41 08	+15·2	−17·1	42 31	+15·0	−16·8
43 59	+15·3	−17·0	45 31	+15·1	−16·7
47 10	+15·4	−16·9	48 55	+15·2	−16·6
50 46	+15·5	−16·8	52 44	+15·3	−16·5
54 49	+15·6	−16·7	57 02	+15·4	−16·4
59 23	+15·7	−16·6	61 51	+15·5	−16·3
64 30	+15·8	−16·5	67 17	+15·6	−16·2
70 12	+15·9	−16·4	73 16	+15·7	−16·1
76 26	+16·0	−16·3	79 43	+15·8	−16·0
83 05	+16·1	−16·2	86 32	+15·9	−15·9
90 00			90 00		

STARS AND PLANETS

App. Alt.	Corrn
9 56	−5·3
10 08	−5·2
10 20	−5·1
10 33	−5·0
10 46	−4·9
11 00	−4·8
11 14	−4·7
11 29	−4·6
11 45	−4·5
12 01	−4·4
12 18	−4·3
12 35	−4·2
12 54	−4·1
13 13	−4·0
13 33	−3·9
13 54	−3·8
14 16	−3·7
14 40	−3·6
15 04	−3·5
15 30	−3·4
15 57	−3·3
16 26	−3·2
16 56	−3·1
17 28	−3·0
18 02	−2·9
18 38	−2·8
19 17	−2·7
19 58	−2·6
20 42	−2·5
21 28	−2·4
22 19	−2·3
23 13	−2·2
24 11	−2·1
25 14	−2·0
26 22	−1·9
27 36	−1·8
28 56	−1·7
30 24	−1·6
32 00	−1·5
33 45	−1·4
35 40	−1·3
37 48	−1·2
40 08	−1·1
42 44	−1·0
45 36	−0·9
48 47	−0·8
52 18	−0·7
56 11	−0·6
60 28	−0·5
65 08	−0·4
70 11	−0·3
75 34	−0·2
81 13	−0·1
87 03	0·0
90 00	

App. Alt. — Additional Corrn

1997

VENUS

Jan. 1–Sept. 26

° ′	
0	+0·1
60	

Sept. 27–Nov. 16

° ′	
0	+0·2
41	+0·1
76	

Nov. 17–Dec. 10

° ′	
0	+0·3
34	+0·2
60	+0·1
80	

Dec. 11–Dec. 25

° ′	
0	+0·4
29	+0·3
51	+0·2
68	+0·1
83	

Dec. 26–Dec. 31

° ′	
0	+0·5
26	+0·4
46	+0·3
60	+0·2
73	+0·1
84	

MARS

Jan. 1–Jan. 20
May 25–Dec. 31

° ′	
0	+0·1
60	

Jan. 21–May 24

° ′	
0	+0·2
41	+0·1
76	

DIP

Ht. of Eye (m)	Corrn	Ht. of Eye (ft.)
2·4	−2·8	8·0
2·6	−2·9	8·6
2·8	−3·0	9·2
3·0	−3·1	9·8
3·2	−3·2	10·5
3·4	−3·3	11·2
3·6	−3·4	11·9
3·8	−3·5	12·6
4·0	−3·6	13·3
4·3	−3·7	14·1
4·5	−3·8	14·9
4·7	−3·9	15·7
5·0	−4·0	16·5
5·2	−4·1	17·4
5·5	−4·2	18·3
5·8	−4·3	19·1
6·1	−4·4	20·1
6·3	−4·5	21·0
6·6	−4·6	22·0
6·9	−4·7	22·9
7·2	−4·8	23·9
7·5	−4·9	24·9
7·9	−5·0	26·0
8·2	−5·1	27·1
8·5	−5·2	28·1
8·8	−5·3	29·2
9·2	−5·4	30·4
9·5	−5·5	31·5
9·9	−5·6	32·7
10·3	−5·7	33·9
10·6	−5·8	35·1
11·0	−5·9	36·3
11·4	−6·0	37·6
11·8	−6·1	38·9
12·2	−6·2	40·1
12·6	−6·3	41·5
13·0	−6·4	42·8
13·4	−6·5	44·2
13·8	−6·6	45·5
14·2	−6·7	46·9
14·7	−6·8	48·4
15·1	−6·9	49·8
15·5	−7·0	51·3
16·0	−7·1	52·8
16·5	−7·2	54·3
16·9	−7·3	55·8
17·4	−7·4	57·4
17·9	−7·5	58·9
18·4	−7·6	60·5
18·8	−7·7	62·1
19·3	−7·8	63·8
19·8	−7·9	65·4
20·4	−8·0	67·1
20·9	−8·1	68·8
21·4		70·5

Ht. of Eye — Corrn (See table)

m	Corrn
1·0	− 1·8
1·5	− 2·2
2·0	− 2·5
2·5	− 2·8
3·0	− 3·0

See table ←

m	Corrn
20	− 7·9
22	− 8·3
24	− 8·6
26	− 9·0
28	− 9·3
30	− 9·6
32	− 10·0
34	− 10·3
36	− 10·6
38	− 10·8
40	− 11·1
42	− 11·4
44	− 11·7
46	− 11·9
48	− 12·2

ft.	Corrn
2	− 1·4
4	− 1·9
6	− 2·4
8	− 2·7
10	− 3·1

See table ←

ft.	Corrn
70	− 8·1
75	− 8·4
80	− 8·7
85	− 8·9
90	− 9·2
95	− 9·5
100	− 9·7
105	− 9·9
110	− 10·2
115	− 10·4
120	− 10·6
125	− 10·8
130	− 11·1
135	− 11·3
140	− 11·5
145	− 11·7
150	− 11·9
155	− 12·1

App. Alt. = Apparent altitude = Sextant altitude corrected for index error and dip.

Appendix E

ALTITUDE CORRECTION TABLES 0°–35°—MOON

App. Alt.	0°–4° Corrⁿ	5°–9° Corrⁿ	10°–14° Corrⁿ	15°–19° Corrⁿ	20°–24° Corrⁿ	25°–29° Corrⁿ	30°–34° Corrⁿ	App. Alt.
00	0 33·8	5 58·2	10 62·1	15 62·8	20 62·2	25 60·8	30 58·9	00
10	35·9	58·5	62·2	62·8	62·1	60·8	58·8	10
20	37·8	58·7	62·2	62·8	62·1	60·7	58·8	20
30	39·6	58·9	62·3	62·8	62·1	60·7	58·7	30
40	41·2	59·1	62·3	62·8	62·0	60·6	58·6	40
50	42·6	59·3	62·4	62·7	62·0	60·6	58·5	50
00	1 44·0	6 59·5	11 62·4	16 62·7	21 62·0	26 60·5	31 58·5	00
10	45·2	59·7	62·4	62·7	61·9	60·4	58·4	10
20	46·3	59·9	62·5	62·7	61·9	60·4	58·3	20
30	47·3	60·0	62·5	62·7	61·9	60·3	58·2	30
40	48·3	60·2	62·5	62·7	61·8	60·3	58·2	40
50	49·2	60·3	62·6	62·7	61·8	60·2	58·1	50
00	2 50·0	7 60·5	12 62·6	17 62·7	22 61·7	27 60·1	32 58·0	00
10	50·8	60·6	62·6	62·6	61·7	60·1	57·9	10
20	51·4	60·7	62·6	62·6	61·6	60·0	57·8	20
30	52·1	60·9	62·7	62·6	61·6	59·9	57·8	30
40	52·7	61·0	62·7	62·6	61·5	59·9	57·7	40
50	53·3	61·1	62·7	62·6	61·5	59·8	57·6	50
00	3 53·8	8 61·2	13 62·7	18 62·5	23 61·5	28 59·7	33 57·5	00
10	54·3	61·3	62·7	62·5	61·4	59·7	57·4	10
20	54·8	61·4	62·7	62·5	61·4	59·6	57·4	20
30	55·2	61·5	62·8	62·5	61·3	59·6	57·3	30
40	55·6	61·6	62·8	62·4	61·3	59·5	57·2	40
50	56·0	61·6	62·8	62·4	61·2	59·4	57·1	50
00	4 56·4	9 61·7	14 62·8	19 62·4	24 61·2	29 59·3	34 57·0	00
10	56·7	61·8	62·8	62·3	61·1	59·3	56·9	10
20	57·1	61·9	62·8	62·3	61·1	59·2	56·9	20
30	57·4	61·9	62·8	62·3	61·0	59·1	56·8	30
40	57·7	62·0	62·8	62·2	60·9	59·1	56·7	40
50	57·9	62·1	62·8	62·2	60·9	59·0	56·6	50

H.P.	L U	L U	L U	L U	L U	L U	L U	H.P.
54·0	0·3 0·9	0·3 0·9	0·4 1·0	0·5 1·1	0·6 1·2	0·7 1·3	0·9 1·5	54·0
54·3	0·7 1·1	0·7 1·2	0·7 1·2	0·8 1·3	0·9 1·4	1·1 1·5	1·2 1·7	54·3
54·6	1·1 1·4	1·1 1·4	1·1 1·4	1·2 1·5	1·3 1·6	1·4 1·7	1·5 1·8	54·6
54·9	1·4 1·6	1·5 1·6	1·5 1·6	1·6 1·7	1·6 1·8	1·8 1·9	1·9 2·0	54·9
55·2	1·8 1·8	1·8 1·8	1·9 1·9	1·9 1·9	2·0 2·0	2·1 2·1	2·2 2·2	55·2
55·5	2·2 2·0	2·2 2·0	2·3 2·1	2·3 2·1	2·4 2·2	2·4 2·3	2·5 2·4	55·5
55·8	2·6 2·2	2·6 2·2	2·6 2·3	2·7 2·3	2·7 2·4	2·8 2·4	2·9 2·5	55·8
56·1	3·0 2·4	3·0 2·5	3·0 2·5	3·0 2·5	3·1 2·6	3·1 2·6	3·2 2·7	56·1
56·4	3·4 2·7	3·4 2·7	3·4 2·7	3·4 2·7	3·4 2·8	3·5 2·8	3·5 2·9	56·4
56·7	3·7 2·9	3·7 2·9	3·8 2·9	3·8 2·9	3·8 3·0	3·8 3·0	3·9 3·0	56·7
57·0	4·1 3·1	4·1 3·1	4·1 3·1	4·1 3·1	4·2 3·1	4·2 3·2	4·2 3·2	57·0
57·3	4·5 3·3	4·5 3·3	4·5 3·3	4·5 3·3	4·5 3·3	4·5 3·4	4·6 3·4	57·3
57·6	4·9 3·5	4·9 3·5	4·9 3·5	4·9 3·5	4·9 3·5	4·9 3·5	4·9 3·6	57·6
57·9	5·3 3·8	5·3 3·8	5·3 3·8	5·2 3·7	5·2 3·7	5·2 3·7	5·2 3·7	57·9
58·2	5·6 4·0	5·6 4·0	5·6 4·0	5·6 4·0	5·6 3·9	5·6 3·9	5·6 3·9	58·2
58·5	6·0 4·2	6·0 4·2	6·0 4·2	6·0 4·2	6·0 4·1	5·9 4·1	5·9 4·1	58·5
58·8	6·4 4·4	6·4 4·4	6·4 4·4	6·3 4·4	6·3 4·3	6·3 4·3	6·2 4·2	58·8
59·1	6·8 4·6	6·8 4·6	6·7 4·6	6·7 4·6	6·7 4·5	6·6 4·5	6·6 4·4	59·1
59·4	7·2 4·8	7·1 4·8	7·1 4·8	7·1 4·8	7·0 4·7	7·0 4·7	6·9 4·6	59·4
59·7	7·5 5·1	7·5 5·0	7·5 5·0	7·5 5·0	7·4 4·9	7·3 4·8	7·2 4·7	59·7
60·0	7·9 5·3	7·9 5·3	7·9 5·2	7·8 5·2	7·8 5·1	7·7 5·0	7·6 4·9	60·0
60·3	8·3 5·5	8·3 5·5	8·2 5·4	8·2 5·4	8·1 5·3	8·0 5·2	7·9 5·1	60·3
60·6	8·7 5·7	8·7 5·7	8·6 5·7	8·6 5·6	8·5 5·5	8·4 5·4	8·2 5·3	60·6
60·9	9·1 5·9	9·0 5·9	9·0 5·9	8·9 5·8	8·8 5·7	8·7 5·6	8·6 5·4	60·9
61·2	9·5 6·2	9·4 6·1	9·4 6·1	9·3 6·0	9·2 5·9	9·1 5·8	8·9 5·6	61·2
61·5	9·8 6·4	9·8 6·3	9·7 6·3	9·7 6·2	9·5 6·1	9·4 5·9	9·2 5·8	61·5

DIP

Ht. of Eye (m)	Corrⁿ	Ht. of Eye (ft)	Ht. of Eye (m)	Corrⁿ	Ht. of Eye (ft)
2·4	−2·8	8·0	9·5	−5·5	31·5
2·6	−2·9	8·6	9·9	−5·6	32·7
2·8	−3·0	9·2	10·3	−5·7	33·9
3·0	−3·1	9·8	10·6	−5·8	35·1
3·2	−3·2	10·5	11·0	−5·9	36·3
3·4	−3·3	11·2	11·4	−6·0	37·6
3·6	−3·4	11·9	11·8	−6·1	38·9
3·8	−3·5	12·6	12·2	−6·2	40·1
4·0	−3·6	13·3	12·6	−6·3	41·5
4·3	−3·7	14·1	13·0	−6·4	42·8
4·5	−3·8	14·9	13·4	−6·5	44·2
4·7	−3·9	15·7	13·8	−6·6	45·5
5·0	−4·0	16·5	14·2	−6·7	46·9
5·2	−4·1	17·4	14·7	−6·8	48·4
5·5	−4·2	18·3	15·1	−6·9	49·8
5·8	−4·3	19·1	15·5	−7·0	51·3
6·1	−4·4	20·1	16·0	−7·1	52·8
6·3	−4·5	21·0	16·5	−7·2	54·3
6·6	−4·6	22·0	16·9	−7·3	55·8
6·9	−4·7	22·9	17·4	−7·4	57·4
7·2	−4·8	23·9	17·9	−7·5	58·9
7·5	−4·9	24·9	18·4	−7·6	60·5
7·9	−5·0	26·0	18·8	−7·7	62·1
8·2	−5·1	27·1	19·3	−7·8	63·8
8·5	−5·2	28·1	19·8	−7·9	65·4
8·8	−5·3	29·2	20·4	−8·0	67·1
9·2	−5·4	30·4	20·9	−8·1	68·8
9·5		31·5	21·4		70·5

MOON CORRECTION TABLE

The correction is in two parts; the first correction is taken from the upper part of the table with argument apparent altitude, and the second from the lower part, with argument H.P., in the same column as that from which the first correction was taken. Separate corrections are given in the lower part for lower (L) and upper (U) limbs. All corrections are to be **added** to apparent altitude, *but 30′ is to be subtracted from the altitude of the upper limb.*

For corrections for pressure and temperature see page A4.

For bubble sextant observations ignore dip, take the mean of upper and lower limb corrections and subtract 15′ from the altitude.

App. Alt. = Apparent altitude = Sextant altitude corrected for index error and dip.

These pages (reduced) are produced from *The Nautical Almanac*.

Appendix E

ALTITUDE CORRECTION TABLES 35°–90°—MOON

App. Alt.	35°–39° Corrⁿ	40°–44° Corrⁿ	45°–49° Corrⁿ	50°–54° Corrⁿ	55°–59° Corrⁿ	60°–64° Corrⁿ	65°–69° Corrⁿ	70°–74° Corrⁿ	75°–79° Corrⁿ	80°–84° Corrⁿ	85°–89° Corrⁿ	App. Alt.
00	35° 56.5	40° 53.7	45° 50.5	50° 46.9	55° 43.1	60° 38.9	65° 34.6	70° 30.1	75° 25.3	80° 20.5	85° 15.6	00
10	56.4	53.6	50.4	46.8	42.9	38.8	34.4	29.9	25.2	20.4	15.5	10
20	56.3	53.5	50.2	46.7	42.8	38.7	34.3	29.7	25.0	20.2	15.3	20
30	56.2	53.4	50.1	46.5	42.7	38.5	34.1	29.6	24.9	20.0	15.1	30
40	56.2	53.3	50.0	46.4	42.5	38.4	34.0	29.4	24.7	19.9	15.0	40
50	56.1	53.2	49.9	46.3	42.4	38.2	33.8	29.3	24.5	19.7	14.8	50
00	36° 56.0	41° 53.1	46° 49.8	51° 46.2	56° 42.3	61° 38.1	66° 33.7	71° 29.1	76° 24.4	81° 19.6	86° 14.6	00
10	55.9	53.0	49.7	46.0	42.1	37.9	33.5	29.0	24.2	19.4	14.5	10
20	55.8	52.8	49.5	45.9	42.0	37.8	33.4	28.8	24.1	19.2	14.3	20
30	55.7	52.7	49.4	45.8	41.8	37.7	33.2	28.7	23.9	19.1	14.1	30
40	55.6	52.6	49.3	45.7	41.7	37.5	33.1	28.5	23.8	18.9	14.0	40
50	55.5	52.5	49.2	45.5	41.6	37.4	32.9	28.3	23.6	18.7	13.8	50
00	37° 55.4	42° 52.4	47° 49.1	52° 45.4	57° 41.4	62° 37.2	67° 32.8	72° 28.2	77° 23.4	82° 18.6	87° 13.7	00
10	55.3	52.3	49.0	45.3	41.3	37.1	32.6	28.0	23.3	18.4	13.5	10
20	55.2	52.2	48.8	45.2	41.2	36.9	32.5	27.9	23.1	18.2	13.3	20
30	55.1	52.1	48.7	45.0	41.0	36.8	32.3	27.7	22.9	18.1	13.2	30
40	55.0	52.0	48.6	44.9	40.9	36.6	32.2	27.6	22.8	17.9	13.0	40
50	55.0	51.9	48.5	44.8	40.8	36.5	32.0	27.4	22.6	17.8	12.8	50
00	38° 54.9	43° 51.8	48° 48.4	53° 44.6	58° 40.6	63° 36.4	68° 31.9	73° 27.2	78° 22.5	83° 17.6	88° 12.7	00
10	54.8	51.7	48.2	44.5	40.5	36.2	31.7	27.1	22.3	17.4	12.5	10
20	54.7	51.6	48.1	44.4	40.3	36.1	31.6	26.9	22.1	17.3	12.3	20
30	54.6	51.5	48.0	44.2	40.2	35.9	31.4	26.8	22.0	17.1	12.2	30
40	54.5	51.4	47.9	44.1	40.1	35.8	31.3	26.6	21.8	16.9	12.0	40
50	54.4	51.2	47.8	44.0	39.9	35.6	31.1	26.5	21.7	16.8	11.8	50
00	39° 54.3	44° 51.1	49° 47.6	54° 43.9	59° 39.8	64° 35.5	69° 31.0	74° 26.3	79° 21.5	84° 16.6	89° 11.7	00
10	54.2	51.0	47.5	43.7	39.6	35.3	30.8	26.1	21.3	16.5	11.5	10
20	54.1	50.9	47.4	43.6	39.5	35.2	30.7	26.0	21.2	16.3	11.4	20
30	54.0	50.8	47.3	43.5	39.4	35.0	30.5	25.8	21.0	16.1	11.2	30
40	53.9	50.7	47.2	43.3	39.2	34.9	30.4	25.7	20.9	16.0	11.0	40
50	53.8	50.6	47.0	43.2	39.1	34.7	30.2	25.5	20.7	15.8	10.9	50

H.P.	L U	L U	L U	L U	L U	L U	L U	L U	L U	L U	L U	H.P.
54.0	1.1 1.7	1.3 1.9	1.5 2.1	1.7 2.4	2.0 2.6	2.3 2.9	2.6 3.2	2.9 3.5	3.2 3.8	3.5 4.1	3.8 4.5	54.0
54.3	1.4 1.8	1.6 2.0	1.8 2.2	2.0 2.5	2.3 2.7	2.5 3.0	2.8 3.2	3.0 3.5	3.3 3.8	3.6 4.1	3.9 4.4	54.3
54.6	1.7 2.0	1.9 2.2	2.1 2.4	2.3 2.6	2.5 2.8	2.7 3.0	3.0 3.3	3.2 3.5	3.5 3.8	3.7 4.1	4.0 4.3	54.6
54.9	2.0 2.2	2.2 2.3	2.3 2.5	2.5 2.7	2.7 2.9	2.9 3.1	3.1 3.3	3.4 3.5	3.6 3.8	3.9 4.0	4.1 4.3	54.9
55.2	2.3 2.3	2.5 2.4	2.6 2.6	2.8 2.8	3.0 2.9	3.2 3.1	3.4 3.3	3.6 3.5	3.8 3.7	4.0 4.0	4.2 4.2	55.2
55.5	2.7 2.5	2.8 2.6	2.9 2.7	3.1 2.9	3.2 3.0	3.4 3.2	3.6 3.4	3.7 3.5	3.9 3.7	4.1 3.9	4.3 4.1	55.5
55.8	3.0 2.6	3.1 2.7	3.2 2.8	3.3 3.0	3.5 3.1	3.6 3.3	3.8 3.4	3.9 3.6	4.1 3.7	4.2 3.9	4.4 4.0	55.8
56.1	3.3 2.8	3.4 2.9	3.5 3.0	3.6 3.1	3.7 3.2	3.8 3.3	4.0 3.4	4.1 3.6	4.2 3.7	4.4 3.8	4.5 4.0	56.1
56.4	3.6 2.9	3.7 3.0	3.8 3.1	3.9 3.2	3.9 3.3	4.0 3.4	4.1 3.5	4.3 3.6	4.4 3.7	4.5 3.8	4.6 3.9	56.4
56.7	3.9 3.1	4.0 3.1	4.1 3.2	4.1 3.3	4.2 3.3	4.3 3.4	4.3 3.5	4.4 3.6	4.5 3.7	4.6 3.8	4.7 3.8	56.7
57.0	4.3 3.2	4.3 3.3	4.3 3.3	4.4 3.4	4.4 3.4	4.5 3.5	4.5 3.5	4.6 3.6	4.7 3.6	4.7 3.7	4.8 3.8	57.0
57.3	4.6 3.4	4.6 3.4	4.6 3.4	4.6 3.5	4.7 3.5	4.7 3.6	4.8 3.6	4.8 3.6	4.8 3.7	4.9 3.7	4.9 3.7	57.3
57.6	4.9 3.6	4.9 3.6	4.9 3.6	4.9 3.6	4.9 3.6	4.9 3.6	4.9 3.6	4.9 3.6	5.0 3.6	5.0 3.6	5.0 3.6	57.6
57.9	5.2 3.7	5.2 3.7	5.2 3.7	5.2 3.7	5.2 3.7	5.1 3.6	5.1 3.6	5.1 3.6	5.1 3.6	5.1 3.6	5.1 3.6	57.9
58.2	5.5 3.9	5.5 3.8	5.5 3.8	5.4 3.8	5.4 3.7	5.4 3.7	5.3 3.7	5.3 3.7	5.2 3.6	5.2 3.6	5.2 3.5	58.2
58.5	5.9 4.0	5.8 4.0	5.8 3.9	5.7 3.9	5.6 3.8	5.6 3.8	5.5 3.7	5.5 3.6	5.4 3.6	5.3 3.5	5.3 3.4	58.5
58.8	6.2 4.2	6.1 4.1	6.0 4.1	6.0 4.0	5.9 3.9	5.8 3.8	5.7 3.7	5.6 3.6	5.5 3.5	5.4 3.5	5.3 3.4	58.8
59.1	6.5 4.3	6.4 4.3	6.3 4.2	6.2 4.1	6.1 4.0	6.0 3.9	5.9 3.8	5.8 3.6	5.7 3.5	5.6 3.4	5.4 3.3	59.1
59.4	6.8 4.5	6.7 4.4	6.6 4.3	6.5 4.2	6.4 4.1	6.2 3.9	6.1 3.8	6.0 3.7	5.8 3.5	5.7 3.4	5.5 3.2	59.4
59.7	7.1 4.6	7.0 4.5	6.9 4.4	6.8 4.3	6.6 4.1	6.5 4.0	6.3 3.8	6.2 3.7	6.0 3.5	5.8 3.3	5.6 3.2	59.7
60.0	7.5 4.8	7.3 4.7	7.2 4.5	7.0 4.4	6.9 4.2	6.7 4.0	6.5 3.9	6.3 3.7	6.1 3.5	5.9 3.3	5.7 3.1	60.0
60.3	7.8 5.0	7.6 4.8	7.5 4.7	7.3 4.5	7.1 4.3	6.9 4.1	6.7 3.9	6.5 3.7	6.3 3.5	6.0 3.2	5.8 3.0	60.3
60.6	8.1 5.1	7.9 5.0	7.7 4.8	7.6 4.6	7.6 4.4	7.3 4.2	7.1 4.0	6.9 3.7	6.6 3.4	6.3 3.2	5.9 2.9	60.6
60.9	8.4 5.3	8.2 5.1	8.0 4.9	7.8 4.7	7.6 4.5	7.3 4.2	7.1 4.0	6.8 3.7	6.6 3.3	6.3 3.2	6.0 2.9	60.9
61.2	8.7 5.4	8.5 5.2	8.3 5.0	8.1 4.8	7.8 4.5	7.6 4.3	7.3 4.0	7.0 3.7	6.7 3.4	6.4 3.1	6.1 2.8	61.2
61.5	9.1 5.6	8.8 5.4	8.6 5.1	8.3 4.9	8.1 4.6	7.8 4.3	7.5 4.0	7.2 3.7	6.9 3.4	6.5 3.1	6.2 2.7	61.5

Appendix F

LAT 52°

N. Lat. {LHA greater than 180°........ Zn=Z; LHA less than 180°.......... Zn=360—Z}

DECLINATION (15°-29°) CONTRARY NAME TO LATITUDE

LHA	15°			16°			17°			18°			19°		
	Hc	d	Z	Hc	d	Z	Hc	d	Z	Hc	d	Z	Hc	d	Z
	° ′	′	°	° ′	′	°	° ′	′	°	° ′	′	°	° ′	′	°
69	00 32	50	116	-0 18	49	116	-1 07	49	117	-1 56	49	117	-2 45	49	118
68	01 05	50	116	00 15	49	117	-0 34	49	118	-1 23	49	118	-2 12	50	119
67	01 38	50	117	00 48	49	118	-0 01	50	118	-0 51	49	119	-1 40	49	119
66	02 10	49	118	01 21	50	119	00 31	49	119	-0 18	50	120	-1 08	50	120
65	02 43	-50	119	01 53	-50	119	01 03	49	120	00 14	-50	120	-0 36	-50	121
64	03 15	50	120	02 25	50	120	01 35	50	121	00 45	50	121	-0 05	50	122
63	03 47	50	120	02 57	50	121	02 07	50	121	01 17	50	122	00 27	51	123
62	04 19	50	121	03 29	51	122	02 38	50	122	01 48	50	123	00 58	51	123
61	04 50	50	122	04 00	51	123	03 09	50	123	02 19	51	124	01 28	50	124
60	05 22	-51	123	04 31	-51	123	03 40	-51	124	02 49	-50	124	01 59	-51	125
59	05 52	50	124	05 02	51	124	04 11	51	125	03 20	51	125	02 29	51	126
58	06 23	51	125	05 32	51	125	04 41	51	126	03 50	51	126	02 59	52	127
57	06 53	51	125	06 02	51	126	05 11	52	126	04 19	51	127	03 28	51	127
56	07 23	51	126	06 32	52	127	05 40	51	127	04 49	52	128	03 57	51	128
55	07 53	-52	127	07 01	-51	128	06 10	-52	128	05 18	-52	129	04 26	-52	129
54	08 22	52	128	07 30	51	128	06 39	52	129	05 47	52	129	04 55	52	130
53	08 51	52	129	07 57	52	129	07 07	52	130	06 15	52	130	05 23	52	131
52	09 20	52	130	08 28	53	130	07 35	52	131	06 43	52	131	05 51	53	132
51	09 48	52	130	08 56	53	131	08 03	52	131	07 11	53	132	06 18	52	132
50	10 16	-52	131	09 24	-53	132	08 31	-53	132	07 38	-53	133	06 45	-52	133
49	10 44	53	132	09 51	53	133	08 58	53	133	08 05	53	134	07 12	53	134
48	11 11	53	133	10 18	53	133	09 25	53	134	08 32	53	134	07 39	54	135
47	11 38	53	134	10 45	54	134	09 51	53	135	08 58	54	135	08 04	53	136
46	12 04	53	135	11 11	54	135	10 17	53	136	09 24	54	136	08 30	54	137
45	12 30	-53	136	11 37	-54	136	10 43	-54	137	09 49	-54	137	08 55	-54	137
44	12 56	54	137	12 02	54	137	11 08	54	137	10 14	54	138	09 20	54	138
43	13 21	54	137	12 27	54	138	11 33	54	138	10 39	55	139	09 44	54	139
42	13 46	54	138	12 52	55	139	11 57	54	139	11 03	55	140	10 08	54	140
41	14 10	54	139	13 16	55	140	12 21	54	140	11 27	55	141	10 32	55	141
40	14 34	-54	140	13 40	-55	141	12 45	-55	141	11 50	-55	141	10 55	-55	142
39	14 58	55	141	14 03	55	141	13 08	55	142	12 13	55	142	11 18	55	143
38	15 21	55	142	14 26	56	142	13 30	55	143	12 35	55	143	11 40	55	144
37	15 43	55	143	14 48	55	143	13 53	56	144	12 57	55	144	12 02	56	144
36	16 05	55	144	15 10	56	144	14 14	55	145	13 19	56	145	12 23	56	145
35	16 27	-56	145	15 31	-56	145	14 35	-55	146	13 40	-56	146	12 44	-56	146
34	16 48	56	146	15 52	56	146	14 56	56	146	14 00	56	147	13 04	56	147
33	17 09	56	147	16 13	57	147	15 16	56	147	14 20	56	148	13 24	57	148
32	17 29	57	148	16 32	56	148	15 36	56	148	14 40	57	149	13 43	57	149
31	17 48	56	149	16 52	57	149	15 55	56	149	14 59	57	150	14 02	57	150
30	18 07	-56	150	17 11	-57	150	16 14	-57	150	15 17	-57	151	14 20	-57	151
29	18 26	57	150	17 29	57	151	16 32	57	151	15 35	57	151	14 38	57	152
28	18 44	57	151	17 47	57	152	16 50	58	152	15 52	57	152	14 55	57	153
27	19 01	57	152	18 04	57	153	17 07	58	153	16 09	57	153	15 12	58	154
26	19 18	57	153	18 21	58	154	17 23	57	154	16 26	58	154	15 28	58	155
25	19 34	-57	154	18 37	-58	155	17 39	-58	155	16 41	-57	155	15 44	-58	156
24	19 50	58	155	18 52	58	156	17 54	57	156	16 57	58	156	15 59	58	156
23	20 05	58	156	19 07	58	157	18 09	58	157	17 11	58	157	16 13	58	157
22	20 20	58	157	19 22	59	158	18 23	58	158	17 25	58	158	16 27	58	158
21	20 34	59	158	19 35	58	159	18 37	58	159	17 39	59	159	16 40	58	159
20	20 47	-58	159	19 49	-59	160	18 50	-58	160	17 52	-59	160	16 53	-58	160
19	21 00	59	160	20 01	58	161	19 03	59	161	18 04	59	161	17 05	58	161
18	21 12	59	161	20 13	58	162	19 15	59	162	18 16	59	162	17 17	59	162
17	21 24	59	162	20 25	59	163	19 26	59	163	18 27	59	163	17 28	59	163
16	21 34	59	163	20 35	59	164	19 36	59	164	18 37	59	164	17 38	59	164
15	21 45	-59	164	20 46	-60	165	19 46	-59	165	18 47	-59	165	17 48	-59	165
14	21 54	59	165	20 55	59	166	19 56	59	166	18 57	60	166	17 57	59	166
13	22 03	59	166	21 04	59	167	20 05	60	167	19 05	59	167	18 06	59	167
12	22 12	60	168	21 12	59	168	20 13	60	168	19 13	59	168	18 14	60	168
11	22 19	59	169	21 20	60	169	20 20	59	169	19 21	60	169	18 21	59	169
10	22 26	-59	170	21 27	-60	170	20 27	-59	170	19 28	-60	170	18 28	-60	170
9	22 33	60	171	21 33	60	171	20 33	59	171	19 34	60	171	18 34	60	171
8	22 38	59	172	21 39	60	172	20 39	60	172	19 39	60	172	18 39	59	172
7	22 44	60	173	21 44	60	173	20 44	60	173	19 44	60	173	18 44	60	173
6	22 48	60	174	21 48	60	174	20 48	60	174	19 48	60	174	18 48	59	174
5	22 52	-60	175	21 52	-60	175	20 52	-60	175	19 52	-60	175	18 52	-60	175
4	22 55	60	176	21 55	60	176	20 55	60	176	19 55	60	176	18 55	60	176
3	22 57	60	177	21 57	60	177	20 57	60	177	19 57	60	177	18 57	60	177
2	22 59	60	178	21 59	60	178	20 59	60	178	19 59	60	178	18 59	60	178
1	23 00	60	179	22 00	60	179	21 00	60	179	20 00	60	179	19 00	60	179
0	23 00	-60	180	22 00	-60	180	21 00	-60	180	20 00	-60	180	19 00	-60	180
	15°			16°			17°			18°			19°		

LHA	20°			21°			22°			23°			24°		
	Hc	d	Z	Hc	d	Z	Hc	d	Z	Hc	d	Z	Hc	d	Z
	° ′	′	°	° ′	′	°	° ′	′	°	° ′	′	°	° ′	′	°
69	-3 34	49	118	-4 23	49	119	-5 12	49	120	-6 01	49	120			
68	-3 02	49	119	-3 51	49	120	-4 40	49	120	-5 29	49	121			
67	-2 29	50	120	-3 19	49	121	-4 08	50	121	-4 58	49	122	-5 47	49	122
66	-1 58	49	121	-2 47	50	121	-3 37	49	122	-4 26	50	122	-5 16	49	123
65	-1 26	-50	122	-2 16	-50	122	-3 06	-49	123	-3 55	-50	123	-4 45	-50	124
64	-0 55	50	122	-1 45	50	123	-2 35	50	123	-3 25	49	124	-4 14	50	125
63	-0 24	50	123	-1 14	50	124	-2 04	50	124	-2 54	50	125	-3 44	50	125
62	00 07	50	124	-0 43	51	124	-1 34	50	125	-2 24	50	126	-3 14	51	126
61	00 38	51	125	-0 13	50	125	-1 03	51	126	-1 54	51	126	-2 45	50	127
60	01 08	-51	126	00 17	-51	126	-0 34	-50	127	-1 24	-51	127	-2 15	-51	128
59	01 38	51	126	00 47	51	127	-0 04	51	127	-0 55	51	128	-1 46	51	128
58	02 07	51	127	01 16	51	128	00 25	51	128	-0 26	51	129	-1 17	51	129
57	02 37	52	128	01 45	51	128	00 54	51	129	00 03	52	129	-0 49	51	130
56	03 06	52	129	02 14	51	129	01 23	52	130	00 31	52	130	-0 21	51	131
55	03 34	-51	130	02 43	-52	130	01 51	-52	131	00 59	-52	131	00 07	-52	132
54	04 03	52	130	03 11	52	131	02 19	52	131	01 27	52	132	00 35	52	132
53	04 31	53	131	03 38	52	132	02 46	52	132	01 54	52	133	01 02	52	133
52	04 58	52	132	04 06	53	132	03 13	52	133	02 21	52	133	01 29	53	134
51	05 26	53	133	04 33	53	133	03 40	52	134	02 48	53	134	01 55	53	135
50	05 53	-53	134	05 00	-53	134	04 07	-53	135	03 14	-53	135	02 21	-53	136
49	06 19	53	135	05 26	53	135	04 33	53	135	03 40	53	136	02 47	53	136
48	06 45	53	135	05 52	53	136	04 59	54	136	04 05	53	137	03 12	53	137
47	07 11	53	136	06 18	54	137	05 24	54	137	04 30	53	138	03 37	54	138
46	07 36	53	137	06 43	54	138	05 49	54	138	04 55	54	138	04 01	53	139
45	08 01	-53	138	07 08	-54	138	06 14	-54	139	05 20	-54	139	04 26	-54	140
44	08 26	54	139	07 32	54	139	06 38	54	140	05 44	55	140	04 49	54	140
43	08 50	54	140	07 56	55	140	07 01	54	140	06 07	54	141	05 13	55	141
42	09 14	55	140	08 19	54	141	07 25	55	141	06 30	54	142	05 36	55	142
41	09 37	55	141	08 42	54	142	07 48	55	142	06 53	55	143	05 58	55	143
40	10 00	-55	142	09 05	-55	143	08 10	-55	143	07 15	-55	143	06 20	-55	144
39	10 23	56	143	09 27	55	143	08 32	55	144	07 37	55	144	06 42	56	145
38	10 45	56	144	09 49	55	144	08 54	56	145	07 58	55	145	07 03	56	146
37	11 06	56	145	10 10	55	145	09 15	56	146	08 19	55	146	07 24	56	146
36	11 27	56	146	10 31	55	146	09 36	56	146	08 40	56	147	07 44	56	147
35	11 48	-56	147	10 52	-56	147	09 56	-56	147	09 00	-56	148	08 04	-56	148
34	12 08	56	148	11 12	57	148	10 15	56	148	09 19	56	149	08 23	56	149
33	12 27	56	148	11 31	56	149	10 35	57	149	09 38	56	149	08 42	57	150
32	12 46	56	149	11 50	57	150	10 53	56	150	09 57	57	150	09 00	57	151
31	13 05	57	150	12 08	56	151	11 12	57	151	10 15	57	151	09 18	57	152
30	13 23	-57	151	12 26	-57	151	11 29	-57	152	10 32	-57	152	09 35	-57	152
29	13 41	57	152	12 44	57	152	11 47	58	153	10 49	57	153	09 52	57	153
28	13 58	57	153	13 01	58	153	12 03	57	154	11 06	57	154	10 09	58	154
27	14 14	57	154	13 17	58	154	12 19	57	155	11 22	58	155	10 24	57	155
26	14 30	57	155	13 33	58	155	12 35	58	155	11 37	57	156	10 40	58	156
25	14 46	-58	156	13 48	-58	156	12 50	-58	156	11 52	-57	157	10 55	-58	157
24	15 01	58	157	14 03	58	157	13 05	58	157	12 07	58	158	11 09	58	158
23	15 15	58	158	14 17	58	158	13 19	58	158	12 21	59	158	11 22	58	159
22	15 29	58	159	14 31	59	159	13 32	58	159	12 34	58	159	11 36	59	160
21	15 42	58	160	14 44	59	160	13 45	58	160	12 47	59	160	11 48	58	161
20	15 55	-59	161	14 56	-58	161	13 58	-59	161	12 59	-59	161	12 00	-58	161
19	16 07	59	161	15 08	59	162	14 09	58	162	13 11	59	162	12 12	59	162
18	16 18	59	162	15 19	58	163	14 21	59	163	13 22	59	163	12 23	59	163
17	16 29	59	163	15 30	59	164	14 31	59	164	13 32	59	164	12 33	59	164
16	16 39	59	164	15 40	59	165	14 41	59	165	13 42	59	165	12 43	59	165
15	16 49	-59	165	15 50	-59	166	14 51	-59	166	13 52	-60	166	12 52	-59	166
14	16 58	59	166	15 59	59	166	15 00	60	167	14 00	59	167	13 01	59	167
13	17 07	60	167	16 07	59	167	15 08	60	168	14 08	59	168	13 09	59	168
12	17 14	59	168	16 15	59	168	15 16	60	169	14 16	59	169	13 17	60	169
11	17 22	60	169	16 22	59	169	15 23	60	169	14 23	60	170	13 23	59	170
10	17 28	-59	170	16 29	-60	170	15 29	-60	170	14 29	-59	171	13 30	-60	171
9	17 34	59	171	16 35	60	171	15 35	60	171	14 35	59	171	13 36	60	172
8	17 40	60	172	16 40	60	172	15 40	60	172	14 40	59	172	13 41	60	173
7	17 44	59	173	16 45	60	173	15 45	60	173	14 45	60	173	13 45	60	173
6	17 49	60	174	16 49	60	174	15 49	60	174	14 49	60	174	13 49	60	174
5	17 52	-60	175	16 52	-60	175	15 52	-60	175	14 52	-60	175	13 52	-59	175
4	17 55	60	176	16 55	60	176	15 55	60	176	14 55	60	176	13 55	60	176
3	17 57	60	177	16 57	60	177	15 57	60	177	14 57	60	177	13 57	60	177
2	17 59	60	178	16 59	60	178	15 59	60	178	14 59	60	178	13 59	60	178
1	18 00	60	179	17 00	60	179	16 00	60	179	15 00	60	179	14 00	60	179
0	18 00	-60	180	17 00	-60	180	16 00	-60	180	15 00	-60	180	14 00	-60	180
	20°			21°			22°			23°			24°		

LHA	25°			26°			27°			28°			29°			LHA
	Hc	d	Z	Hc	d	Z	Hc	d	Z	Hc	d	Z	Hc	d	Z	
	° ′	′	°	° ′	′	°	° ′	′	°	° ′	′	°	° ′	′	°	
69																291
68																292
67																293
66																294
65	-5 35	-49	124													295
64	-5 04	50	125	-5 54	50	126										296
63	-4 34	50	126	-5 24	51	126										297
62	-4 05	50	127	-4 55	50	127	-5 45	50	128							298
61	-3 35	51	127	-4 26	50	128	-5 16	51	128							299
60	-3 06	-51	128	-3 57	-50	129	-4 47	-51	129	-5 38	-51	130				300
59	-2 37	51	129	-3 28	51	129	-4 19	51	130	-5 10	51	130				301
58	-2 08	52	130	-3 00	51	130	-3 51	51	131	-4 42	51	131	-5 33	51	132	302
57	-1 40	52	131	-2 32	51	131	-3 23	51	132	-4 14	52	132	-5 06	51	133	303
56	-1 12	52	131	-2 04	51	132	-2 55	52	132	-3 47	52	133	-4 39	51	133	304
55	-0 45	-51	132	-1 36	-52	133	-2 28	-52	133	-3 20	-52	134	-4 12	-52	134	305
54	-0 17	52	133	-1 09	52	133	-2 01	52	134	-2 53	52	134	-3 45	52	135	306
53	00 10	53	134	-0 43	52	134	-1 35	52	135	-2 27	52	135	-3 19	52	136	307
52	00 36	52	134	-0 16	53	135	-1 09	52	135	-2 01	53	136	-2 54	52	136	308
51	01 02	52	135	00 10	53	136	-0 43	53	136	-1 36	52	137	-2 28	53	137	309
50	01 28	-53	136	00 35	-53	136	-0 18	-53	137	-1 11	-52	137	-2 03	-53	138	310
49	01 54	54	137	01 00	53	137	00 07	53	138	-0 46	53	138	-1 39	53	139	311
48	02 19	54	138	01 25	53	138	00 32	53	139	-0 21	54	139	-1 15	53	139	312
47	02 43	53	138	01 50	54	139	00 56	53	139	00 03	54	140	-0 51	53	140	313
46	03 08	54	139	02 14	54	140	01 20	54	140	00 26	53	141	-0 27	54	141	314
45	03 32	-54	140	02 38	-54	140	01 44	-54	141	00 50	-54	141	-0 04	-54	142	315
44	03 55	54	141	03 01	54	141	02 07	55	142	01 12	54	142	00 18	54	143	316
43	04 18	54	142	03 24	55	142	02 29	54	143	01 35	55	143	00 40	54	143	317
42	04 41	55	143	03 46	54	143	02 52	55	143	01 57	55	144	01 02	54	144	318
41	05 03	55	143	04 08	55	144	03 13	54	144	02 19	55	145	01 24	55	145	319
40	05 25	-55	144	04 30	-55	145	03 35	-55	145	02 40	-55	145	01 45	-55	146	320
39	05 46	55	145	04 51	55	145	03 56	55	146	03 01	56	146	02 05	55	147	321
38	06 07	55	146	05 12	56	146	04 16	55	147	03 21	56	147	02 25	55	147	322
37	06 28	56	147	05 32	55	147	04 37	56	147	03 41	56	148	02 45	56	148	323
36	06 48	56	148	05 52	56	148	04 56	56	148	04 00	56	149	03 04	56	149	324
35	07 08	-57	148	06 11	-56	149	05 15	-56	149	04 19	-56	149	03 23	-56	150	325
34	07 27	57	149	06 30	56	150	05 34	56	150	04 38	57	150	03 41	56	151	326
33	07 45	56	150	06 49	57	151	05 52	56	151	04 56	57	151	03 59	56	151	327
32	08 03	56	151	07 07	57	151	06 10	57	152	05 13	56	152	04 17	57	152	328
31	08 21	57	152	07 24	57	152	06 27	56	153	05 31	57	153	04 34	57	153	329
30	08 38	-57	153	07 41	-57	153	06 44	-57	153	05 47	-57	154	04 50	-57	154	330
29	08 55	57	154	07 58	57	154	07 01	58	154	06 03	57	155	05 06	57	155	331
28	09 11	57	155	08 14	58	155	07 16	57	155	06 19	57	155	05 22	58	156	332
27	09 27	58	155	08 29	57	156	07 32	58	156	06 34	57	156	05 37	58	157	333
26	09 42	58	156	08 44	57	157	07 47	58	157	06 49	58	157	05 51	58	157	334
25	09 57	-58	157	08 59	-58	157	08 01	-58	158	07 03	-58	158	06 05	-58	158	335
24	10 11	58	158	09 13	58	158	08 15	58	159	07 17	58	159	06 19	59	159	336
23	10 24	58	159	09 26	58	159	08 28	58	159	07 30	58	160	06 32	59	160	337
22	10 37	58	160	09 39	58	160	08 41	59	160	07 42	58	161	06 44	58	161	338
21	10 50	59	161	09 51	58	161	08 53	59	161	07 54	58	161	06 56	59	162	339
20	11 02	-59	162	10 03	-58	162	09 05	-59	162	08 06	-59	162	07 07	-58	163	340
19	11 13	59	163	10 14	58	163	09 16	59	163	08 17	59	163	07 18	59	163	341
18	11 24	59	163	10 25	59	164	09 26	59	164	08 27	58	164	07 29	59	164	342
17	11 34	59	164	10 35	59	165	09 36	59	165	08 37	59	165	07 38	59	165	343
16	11 44	59	165	10 45	59	165	09 46	59	166	08 47	59	166	07 48	60	166	344
15	11 53	-59	166	10 54	-59	166	09 55	-60	167	08 55	-59	167	07 56	-59	167	345
14	12 02	60	167	11 02	59	167	10 03	59	167	09 04	60	168	08 04	59	168	346
13	12 10	60	168	11 10	59	168	10 11	60	168	09 11	59	168	08 12	59	169	347
12	12 17	59	169	11 18	60	169	10 18	59	169	09 19	60	169	08 19	59	169	348
11	12 24	60	170	11 24	59	170	10 25	60	170	09 25	59	170	08 26	60	170	349
10	12 30	-59	171	11 31	-60	171	10 31	-60	171	09 31	-59	171	08 32	-60	171	350
9	12 36	60	172	11 36	60	172	10 36	59	172	09 37	60	172	08 37	60	172	351
8	12 41	60	173	11 41	60	173	10 41	59	173	09 42	60	173	08 42	60	173	352
7	12 45	59	174	11 46	60	174	10 46	60	174	09 46	60	174	08 46	60	174	353
6	12 49	60	174	11 49	59	175	10 50	60	175	09 50	60	175	08 50	60	175	354
5	12 53	-60	175	11 53	-60	175	10 53	-60	176	09 53	-60	176	08 53	-60	176	355
4	12 55	60	176	11 55	60	176	10 55	60	176	09 55	60	176	08 55	59	177	356
3	12 57	60	177	11 57	60	177	10 57	60	177	09 57	60	177	08 57	59	177	357
2	12 59	60	178	11 59	60	178	10 59	60	178	09 59	60	178	08 59	60	178	358
1	13 00	60	179	12 00	60	179	11 00	60	179	10 00	60	179	09 00	60	179	359
0	13 00	-60	180	12 00	-60	180	11 00	-60	180	10 00	-60	180	09 00	-60	180	360
	25°			26°			27°			28°			29°			

This table (reduced) is reproduced from AP3270 *Sight Reduction Tables for Air Navigation*, Vol 3.

Appendix G

LAT 40°S

LHA ♈	Hc	Zn	Hc	Zn	Hc	Zn	Hc	Zn	Hc	Zn	Hc	Zn	Hc	Zn
0	20 55	002	20 00	031	14 00	089	27 35	137	51 50	226	26 37	257	31 02	320
1	20 56	001	20 24	030	14 46	088	28 06	137	51 18	226	25 52	256	30 32	319
2	20 56	000	20 46	029	15 32	088	28 38	136	50 45	226	25 07	256	30 02	318
3	20 56	359	21 08	028	16 18	087	29 10	136	50 12	226	24 23	255	29 31	317
4	20 55	358	21 30	027	17 04	086	29 42	136	49 39	226	23 38	255	28 59	316
5	20 53	357	21 51	026	17 50	086	30 14	135	49 06	226	22 54	254	28 27	315
6	20 50	356	22 11	025	18 35	085	30 46	135	48 33	226	22 10	254	27 55	314
7	20 47	355	22 30	025	19 21	084	31 19	135	48 00	226	21 26	253	27 21	313
8	20 43	354	22 49	024	20 07	084	31 51	135	47 27	226	20 42	252	26 48	312
9	20 38	353	23 07	023	20 53	083	32 24	134	46 55	225	19 58	252	26 13	311
10	20 32	353	23 24	022	21 38	082	32 57	134	46 22	225	19 15	251	25 39	311
11	20 26	352	23 41	021	22 24	082	33 31	134	45 49	225	18 31	251	25 04	310
12	20 19	351	23 57	020	23 09	081	34 04	133	45 16	225	17 48	250	24 28	309
13	20 11	350	24 12	019	23 55	080	34 37	133	44 44	225	17 05	250	23 52	308
14	20 03	349	24 27	018	24 40	080	35 11	133	44 11	225	16 22	249	23 16	307
15	24 40	017	14 29	053	25 25	079	35 45	132	43 39	225	62 58	283	19 54	348
16	24 53	016	15 06	052	26 10	078	36 19	132	43 06	225	62 13	282	19 44	347
17	25 06	015	15 42	052	26 55	077	36 53	132	42 34	225	61 28	281	19 33	346
18	25 17	014	16 18	051	27 40	077	37 27	132	42 02	224	60 42	280	19 22	345
19	25 28	013	16 53	050	28 24	076	38 02	131	41 30	224	59 57	279	19 10	344
20	25 38	012	17 28	049	29 09	075	38 36	131	40 58	224	59 12	278	18 57	343
21	25 47	011	18 03	048	29 53	074	39 11	131	40 26	224	58 26	278	18 43	343
22	25 55	010	18 37	048	30 38	074	39 46	131	39 54	224	57 41	277	18 29	342
23	26 02	009	19 11	047	31 22	073	40 20	131	39 22	224	56 55	276	18 14	341
24	26 09	008	19 44	046	32 05	072	40 55	130	38 50	223	56 09	275	17 59	340
25	26 15	007	20 17	045	32 49	071	41 31	130	38 19	223	55 23	275	17 43	339
26	26 20	006	20 49	044	33 32	071	42 06	130	37 47	223	54 38	274	17 26	338
27	26 24	005	21 21	043	34 16	070	42 41	130	37 16	223	53 52	273	17 09	337
28	26 28	004	21 52	043	34 59	069	43 16	130	36 45	223	53 06	272	16 51	336
29	26 31	003	22 23	042	35 41	068	43 52	129	36 14	222	52 20	272	16 32	336
30	26 32	002	22 54	041	36 24	067	24 53	091	44 28	129	35 43	222	51 34	271
31	26 33	001	23 23	040	37 06	066	25 39	091	45 03	129	35 12	222	50 48	270
32	26 34	000	23 53	039	37 48	065	26 25	090	45 39	129	34 41	222	50 02	270
33	26 33	359	24 21	038	38 30	065	27 11	089	46 15	129	34 11	221	49 16	269
34	26 32	358	24 49	037	39 11	064	27 57	089	46 51	129	33 41	221	48 30	269
35	26 29	357	25 17	036	39 52	063	28 43	088	47 27	128	33 10	221	47 44	268
36	26 26	356	25 44	035	40 33	062	29 29	088	48 03	128	32 40	221	46 58	267
37	26 22	355	26 10	034	41 13	061	30 15	087	48 39	128	32 11	220	46 12	267
38	26 17	354	26 36	033	41 53	060	31 01	086	49 15	128	31 41	220	45 26	266
39	26 12	353	27 01	032	42 33	059	31 47	086	49 51	128	31 11	220	44 41	265
40	26 06	352	27 25	031	43 12	058	32 33	085	50 28	128	30 42	220	43 55	265
41	25 58	351	27 49	030	43 51	057	33 18	084	51 04	128	30 13	219	43 09	264
42	25 50	350	28 11	029	44 29	056	34 04	083	51 40	128	29 44	219	42 23	264
43	25 42	349	28 34	028	45 07	055	34 50	083	52 16	128	29 15	219	41 38	263
44	25 32	348	28 55	027	45 44	054	35 35	082	52 53	128	28 47	218	40 52	263
45	29 16	026	46 20	052	36 21	081	53 29	128	68 11	211	40 06	262	25 22	347
46	29 36	025	46 57	051	37 06	081	54 06	128	67 48	212	39 21	262	25 11	346
47	29 56	024	47 32	050	37 51	080	54 42	128	67 23	213	38 36	261	24 59	345
48	30 14	023	48 07	049	38 36	079	55 18	128	66 58	214	37 50	260	24 46	344
49	30 32	022	48 42	048	39 22	078	55 55	128	66 32	214	37 05	260	24 33	343
50	30 49	021	49 15	046	40 06	078	56 31	128	66 06	215	36 20	259	24 19	342
51	31 05	020	49 48	045	40 51	077	57 07	128	65 39	216	35 35	259	24 04	341
52	31 21	019	50 20	044	41 36	076	57 43	128	65 12	217	34 49	258	23 48	340
53	31 35	018	50 52	043	42 20	075	58 20	128	64 44	217	34 05	258	23 32	339
54	31 49	017	51 23	041	43 05	074	58 56	128	64 16	218	33 20	257	23 15	338
55	32 02	016	51 53	040	43 49	073	59 32	128	63 48	219	32 35	257	22 57	337
56	32 14	015	52 22	038	44 33	073	60 08	129	63 19	219	31 50	256	22 39	336
57	32 25	014	52 50	037	45 17	072	60 44	129	62 50	220	31 06	256	22 19	335
58	32 36	012	53 17	036	46 00	071	61 19	129	62 20	220	30 21	255	22 00	334
59	32 45	011	53 43	034	46 43	070	61 55	129	61 50	221	29 37	255	21 39	333
60	32 54	010	35 41	036	47 26	069	21 29	157	61 20	221	28 53	254	21 18	332
61	33 01	009	36 08	035	48 09	068	21 48	157	60 50	221	28 08	254	20 56	331
62	33 08	008	36 34	034	48 52	067	22 06	156	60 19	222	27 24	253	20 34	330
63	33 14	007	36 59	033	49 34	066	22 25	156	59 49	222	26 40	252	20 11	330
64	33 19	006	37 23	031	50 16	065	22 43	156	59 18	222	25 57	252	19 47	329
65	33 23	004	37 47	030	50 57	064	23 03	155	58 47	223	25 13	251	19 23	328
66	33 26	003	38 09	029	51 38	063	23 22	155	58 15	223	24 30	251	18 58	327
67	33 28	002	38 31	028	52 19	062	23 42	155	57 44	223	23 46	250	18 33	326
68	33 30	001	38 53	027	52 59	061	24 01	154	57 12	224	23 03	250	18 07	325
69	33 30	000	39 13	026	53 39	060	24 22	154	56 40	224	22 20	249	17 40	324
70	33 29	359	39 32	024	54 19	058	24 42	154	56 09	224	21 37	249	17 13	323
71	33 28	358	39 51	023	54 57	057	25 03	153	55 37	224	20 54	248	16 46	323
72	33 26	356	40 08	022	55 36	056	25 23	153	55 05	224	20 12	248	16 17	322
73	33 22	355	40 25	021	56 14	055	25 45	153	54 33	224	19 29	247	15 49	321
74	33 18	354	40 41	019	56 51	053	26 06	152	54 00	225	18 47	247	15 20	320
75	40 56	018	57 27	052	44 42	116	26 27	152	53 28	225	31 05	272	33 13	353
76	41 09	017	58 03	050	45 24	115	26 49	152	52 56	225	30 19	271	33 07	352
77	41 22	016	58 38	049	46 05	115	27 11	151	52 23	225	29 33	271	33 00	351
78	41 34	014	59 12	048	46 47	115	27 33	151	51 51	225	28 47	270	32 52	350
79	41 45	013	59 46	046	47 29	114	27 55	151	51 19	225	28 01	269	32 43	348
80	41 55	012	60 19	044	48 11	114	28 18	150	50 46	225	27 15	269	32 34	347
81	42 04	010	60 50	043	48 53	114	28 41	150	50 14	225	26 29	268	32 23	346
82	42 11	009	61 21	041	49 35	113	29 04	150	49 41	225	25 43	267	32 12	345
83	42 18	008	61 51	039	50 17	113	29 27	150	49 09	225	24 57	267	32 00	344
84	42 24	006	62 19	038	50 59	113	29 50	149	48 37	225	24 11	266	31 47	343
85	42 28	005	62 47	036	51 42	113	30 14	149	48 04	225	23 26	266	31 33	342
86	42 32	004	63 13	034	52 24	112	30 37	149	47 32	225	22 40	265	31 18	341
87	42 34	002	63 38	032	53 07	112	31 01	149	46 59	225	21 54	264	31 02	340
88	42 35	001	64 02	030	53 49	112	31 25	148	46 27	225	21 08	264	30 46	339
89	42 36	000	64 24	028	54 32	112	31 50	148	45 55	225	20 23	263	30 29	338

LAT 40°S

LHA ♈	Hc	Zn	Hc	Zn	Hc	Zn	Hc	Zn	Hc	Zn	Hc	Zn	Hc	Zn
90	39 21	033	12 35	062	55 15	111	32 14	148	45 22	225	56 37	339	42 35	358
91	39 45	031	13 16	062	55 58	111	32 38	148	44 50	224	56 20	337	42 33	357
92	40 09	030	13 56	061	56 40	111	33 03	147	44 18	224	56 01	336	42 30	356
93	40 32	029	14 36	060	57 23	111	33 28	147	43 46	224	55 42	334	42 26	354
94	40 54	028	15 16	059	58 06	110	33 53	147	43 14	224	55 21	332	42 21	353
95	41 15	027	15 55	059	58 50	110	34 18	147	42 42	224	54 59	331	42 14	352
96	41 35	025	16 34	058	59 33	110	34 43	147	42 10	224	54 36	329	42 07	350
97	41 54	024	17 13	057	60 16	110	35 09	146	41 38	224	54 12	328	41 59	349
98	42 12	023	17 51	056	60 59	110	35 34	146	41 07	224	53 47	326	41 50	348
99	42 30	022	18 29	055	61 42	110	36 00	146	40 35	223	53 21	325	41 39	346
100	42 46	020	19 07	055	62 26	109	36 26	146	40 04	223	52 54	323	41 28	345
101	43 01	019	19 44	054	63 09	109	36 51	146	39 32	223	52 26	322	41 15	344
102	43 16	018	20 21	053	63 53	109	37 17	145	39 01	223	51 57	320	41 02	342
103	43 29	016	20 58	052	64 36	109	37 44	145	38 30	223	51 27	319	40 48	341
104	43 41	015	21 34	051	65 20	109	38 10	145	37 59	222	50 57	318	40 32	340
105	43 53	014	22 10	051	19 32	097	38 36	145	37 28	222	50 25	316	40 16	339
106	44 03	012	22 45	050	20 17	096	39 02	145	36 57	222	49 53	315	39 59	337
107	44 12	011	23 20	049	21 03	096	39 29	145	36 26	222	49 20	314	39 41	336
108	44 20	009	23 54	048	21 49	095	39 56	145	35 56	222	48 47	312	39 22	335
109	44 27	008	24 28	047	22 35	094	40 22	145	35 25	221	48 12	311	39 02	334
110	44 33	007	25 02	046	23 20	094	40 49	144	34 55	221	47 37	310	38 41	333
111	44 38	005	25 35	045	24 06	093	41 16	144	34 25	221	47 02	309	38 19	331
112	44 41	004	26 07	044	24 52	093	41 43	144	33 55	221	46 26	308	37 57	330
113	44 44	002	26 39	044	25 38	092	42 09	144	33 25	220	45 49	307	37 34	329
114	44 45	001	27 11	043	26 24	091	42 36	144	32 55	220	45 12	305	37 10	328
115	44 46	000	27 41	042	27 10	091	43 03	144	32 26	220	44 34	304	36 45	327
116	44 45	358	28 12	041	27 56	090	43 30	144	31 56	220	43 56	303	36 19	326
117	44 43	357	28 41	040	28 42	089	43 58	144	31 27	219	43 18	302	35 53	325
118	44 40	355	29 10	039	29 28	089	44 25	144	30 58	219	42 39	301	35 26	323
119	44 36	354	29 39	038	30 14	088	44 52	144	30 29	219	41 59	300	34 58	322
120	30 07	037	13 49	093	45 19	144	69 17	224	41 19	299	34 30	321	44 30	353
121	30 34	036	14 35	092	45 46	144	68 44	225	40 39	298	34 01	320	44 24	351
122	31 01	035	15 20	092	46 13	144	68 11	226	39 58	297	33 31	319	44 16	350
123	31 27	034	16 06	091	46 40	144	67 38	226	39 17	296	33 01	318	44 08	349
124	31 52	033	16 52	091	47 08	144	67 05	227	38 36	296	32 30	317	43 58	347
125	32 16	032	17 38	090	47 35	144	66 31	228	37 54	295	31 59	316	43 47	346
126	32 40	031	18 24	089	48 02	144	65 57	228	37 13	294	31 26	315	43 36	344
127	33 03	030	19 10	089	48 29	144	65 23	229	36 30	293	30 54	314	43 23	343
128	33 26	029	19 56	088	48 56	144	64 48	229	35 48	292	30 21	313	43 09	342
129	33 47	027	20 42	087	49 23	144	64 13	229	35 05	291	29 47	312	42 54	340
130	34 08	026	21 28	087	49 50	144	63 38	230	34 22	290	29 13	311	42 38	339
131	34 28	025	22 14	086	50 17	144	63 03	230	33 39	290	28 38	311	42 21	338
132	34 47	024	23 00	085	50 44	144	62 28	230	32 56	289	28 03	310	42 04	337
133	35 05	023	23 45	085	51 11	144	61 52	231	32 12	288	27 27	309	41 45	335
134	35 23	022	24 31	084	51 37	145	61 17	231	31 28	287	26 51	308	41 25	334
135	35 39	021	25 17	083	52 04	145	60 41	231	30 44	286	26 15	307	41 05	333
136	35 55	019	26 03	083	52 30	145	60 05	231	30 00	286	25 38	306	40 43	332
137	36 10	018	26 48	082	52 57	145	59 29	232	29 16	285	25 00	305	40 21	330
138	36 24	017	27 33	081	53 23	145	58 53	232	28 31	284	24 23	304	39 58	329
139	36 37	016	28 19	080	53 49	146	58 17	232	27 46	283	23 45	304	39 34	328
140	36 49	015	29 04	080	54 15	146	57 41	232	27 02	283	23 06	303	39 09	327
141	37 01	014	29 49	079	54 41	146	57 04	232	26 17	282	22 27	302	38 43	326
142	37 11	012	30 34	078	55 06	146	56 28	232	25 32	281	21 48	301	38 17	325
143	37 20	011	31 19	078	55 32	147	55 52	232	24 47	280	21 09	300	37 50	323
144	37 29	010	32 04	077	55 57	147	55 15	232	24 01	280	20 29	300	37 22	322
145	37 36	009	32 49	076	56 22	147	54 39	232	23 16	279	19 49	299	36 54	321
146	37 42	007	33 33	075	56 47	147	54 03	232	22 31	278	19 08	298	36 25	320
147	37 48	006	34 18	075	57 11	148	53 26	232	21 45	278	18 27	297	35 55	319
148	37 52	005	35 02	074	57 36	148	52 50	232	20 59	277	17 46	296	35 24	318
149	37 56	004	35 46	073	58 00	149	52 14	232	20 14	276	17 05	296	34 53	317
150	37 58	003	36 30	072	58 24	149	59 40	188	51 37	232	41 57	284	34 21	316
151	38 00	001	37 13	071	58 47	149	59 33	189	51 01	232	41 12	284	33 49	315
152	38 00	000	37 57	070	59 10	150	59 26	189	50 25	232	40 27	283	33 16	314
153	38 00	359	38 40	070	59 33	150	59 19	190	49 48	232	39 42	282	32 43	313
154	37 59	358	39 23	069	59 56	151	59 10	191	49 12	232	38 57	281	32 09	312
155	37 56	356	40 06	068	60 18	151	59 02	191	48 36	232	38 12	281	31 35	311
156	37 53	355	40 48	067	60 40	152	58 53	192	48 00	232	37 27	280	31 00	310
157	37 48	354	41 30	066	61 01	153	58 43	192	47 24	232	36 42	279	30 24	309
158	37 43	353	42 12	065	61 22	153	58 33	193	46 48	231	35 56	278	29 48	308
159	37 36	351	42 54	064	61 43	154	58 22	194	46 12	231	35 11	278	29 12	307
160	37 29	350	43 35	063	62 03	154	58 11	194	45 36	231	34 25	277	28 35	306
161	37 21	349	44 16	062	62 23	155	58 00	195	45 00	231	33 39	276	27 58	305
162	37 11	348	44 56	061	62 42	156	57 48	195	44 25	231	32 54	275	27 20	305
163	37 01	347	45 36	060	63 00	156	57 36	196	43 49	231	32 08	275	26 42	304
164	36 50	345	46 16	059	63 18	157	57 23	196	43 14	230	31 22	274	26 04	303
165	15 20	048	22 13	107	63 36	158	42 38	230	30 36	273	25 25	302	36 38	344
166	15 54	047	22 58	106	63 53	159	42 03	230	29 50	273	24 46	301	36 25	343
167	16 27	046	23 42	105	64 09	160	41 28	230	29 04	272	24 06	300	36 11	342
168	17 00	045	24 26	105	64 25	160	40 53	230	28 19	271	23 27	300	35 56	341
169	17 32	044	25 11	104	64 40	161	40 18	229	27 33	271	22 47	299	35 40	339
170	18 04	043	25 55	104	64 54	162	39 43	229	26 47	270	22 06	298	35 24	338
171	18 35	043	26 40	103	65 08	163	39 08	229	26 01	270	21 25	297	35 06	337
172	19 06	042	27 25	103	65 21	164	38 33	229	25 15	269	20 44	296	34 48	336
173	19 37	041	28 10	102	65 33	165	37 59	229	24 29	268	20 03	296	34 29	335
174	20 07	040	28 55	102	65 44	166	37 24	228	23 43	268	19 21	295	34 09	334
175	20 36	039	29 40	101	65 55	167	36 50	228	22 57	267	18 40	294	33 48	333
176	21 05	038	30 25	100	66 05	168	36 16	228	22 11	266	17 58	293	33 27	332
177	21 33	038	31 10	100	66 14	169	35 42	227	21 25	266	17 15	293	33 04	330
178	22 01	037	31 55	099	66 22	170	35 08	227	20 39	265	16 33	292	32 41	329
179	22 28	036	32 41	099	66 29	171	34 35	227	19 54	265	15 50	291	32 18	328

This table (reduced) is produced from AP3270 *Sight Reduction Tables for Air Navigation*, Vol 1.

Appendix H

TABLE 5.—Correction to Tabulated Altitude for Minutes of Declination

This table (reduced) is reproduced from AP3270 *Sight Reduction Tables for Air Navigation*, Vol 3.

INDEX